D1156031

THE COMPLETE BOOK OF

HELICOPTERS

Discard
No Longer The Property Of
Memphis/Shelby County Public
Library & Information Center

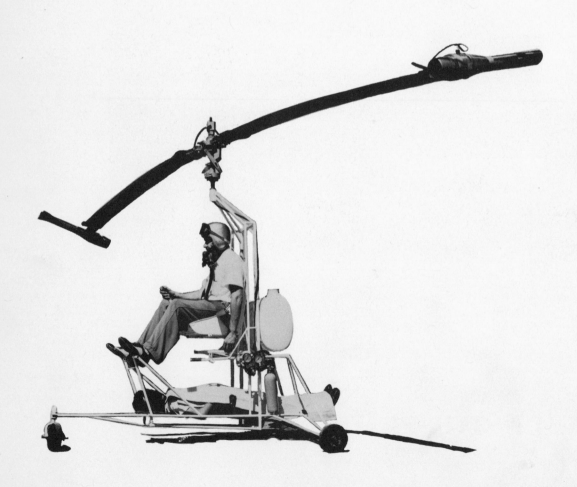

THE COMPLETE BOOK OF

Helicopters

by D. N. AHNSTROM

Managing Editor of "Skyways"

CLEVELAND  NEW YORK

THE WORLD PUBLISHING COMPANY

LIBRARY OF CONGRESS CATALOG CARD NUMBER: 54-8173

Design and typography by Jos. Trautwein

CW

COPYRIGHT 1954 BY THE WORLD PUBLISHING COMPANY.
ALL RIGHTS RESERVED. NO PART OF THIS BOOK MAY BE
REPRODUCED IN ANY FORM WITHOUT WRITTEN PERMISSION FROM
THE PUBLISHER, EXCEPT FOR BRIEF PASSAGES
INCLUDED IN A REVIEW APPEARING IN A NEWSPAPER OR MAGAZINE.
MANUFACTURED IN THE UNITED STATES OF AMERICA.

NORTH
629.1335
A28
27584A
Memphis Public
Library

ACKNOWLEDGMENTS

THE FIRST time I ever rode in a helicopter, I felt as if I were being pogo-sticked in a fishbowl. We took off from the plaza in front of City Hall in Cleveland, Ohio, and heli-hopped over the ball park, down the lake shore and then into the airport. That was several years ago. To the Bell Aircraft Corporation, which was responsible for the ride, I owe a continuing debt of gratitude.

Similarly, I owe a genuine debt to Sikorsky Aircraft, and particularly to Ned Benham, Ralph Lightfoot, William Kilpatrick, and Irene Herrnstadt.

Thanks for help in making this book possible go also to Don Ryan Mockler and Jean Ross Howard of the Helicopter Council; to Herbert Fisher, Philip Landi, Marcel Chevalier and Warren Goodman of the Port of New York Authority; to the Rotor-Aids Company of Ventura, California; to Bill McLeod, Senior Pilot for Okanagan Airways; to Harry Lounsbury, Executive Secretary of the American Helicopter Society; to John Coleman, Public Relations Manager at Bell Aircraft; to William J. Barber, Public Relations Director of Glenview Metal Products Company; and to Howard Levy.

Grateful acknowledgment is also extended to the Defense Department Office of Public Information; to the Office of Chief of Naval Operations; to the U. S. Department of Agriculture Forest Service; to the Information Office of the Canadian Consulate General; and to Paul E. Garber and Robert C. Strobell of the Smithsonian Institution National Air Museum for their very generous co-operation.

My grateful appreciation goes to Samuel L. Blumenfeld of The World Publishing Company for a thorough and imaginative job of editing, picture research, and seeing the book through its many stages of production.

Special thanks to Dr. Roland Spaulding of New York University, an able pilot and affable teacher of aeronautics—that rare kind of teacher who makes it fun to learn.

D. N. AHNSTROM

CONTENTS

PHOTO AND ILLUSTRATION CREDITS

Page 1, Bell Aircraft Corporation; page 2 (top), Sikorsky Aircraft; page 2 (bottom), Howard Levy; page 3, Piasecki Helicopter Corporation; page 6, Department of Defense Photo (Marine Corps); page 8, Official U.S. Marine Corps Photo; page 10, U.S. Army Photo; pages 13, 14, 15, 17 (top and bottom), 18, 19 (top and bottom), 20, Smithsonian Institution National Air Museum; page 21, Igor Sikorsky; pages 22, 23 (top), Smithsonian Institution; page 23 (bottom), Institute of Aeronautical Sciences; page 24, Hiller Helicopters; page 25 (top), Institute of Aeronautical Sciences; pages 25 (bottom), 26, 27, 28 (top and bottom), 29 (top and bottom), Smithsonian Institution; pages 31 (top and bottom), 32, 33, Sikorsky Aircraft; page 34 (top and bottom), United Aircraft Corporation; page 35, Hiller Helicopters; page 36, Don Downie; page 37 (top and bottom), Bell Aircraft Corporation; page 38, Department of Defense Photo; page 39 (top), Kaman Aircraft Corporation; page 39 (bottom), Doman Helicopters, Inc.; page 40, Howard Levy; page 41 (top), Hughes Aircraft Company; page 41 (bottom), U.S. Marine Corps Photo; page 42 (top), McCulloch Aircraft; page 42 (bottom), Penn Elastic Company; page 43 (top), Bell Aircraft Corporation; page 43 (bottom), Kaman Aircraft Corporation; page 44, U.S. Navy Photo; page 45 (top), Piasecki Helicopter Corporation; page 45 (bottom), U.S. Coast Guard Photo; page 46, Sikorsky Aircraft; page 48, Bell Aircraft Corporation; pages 50, 51, 52, 54, 55, U.S. Forest Service; page 56, National Film Board of Canada; page 57 (top), U.S. Coast Guard Photo; pages 57 (bottom), 58, Wilfred Doucette, Ottawa, Canada; pages 60, 61, Hiller Helicopters; pages 63, 64, Bell Aircraft Corporation; page 65, National Film Board of Canada; pages 68, 69, Bell Aircraft Corporation; page 70 (top and bottom), Hiller Helicopters; pages 71, 72, Bell Aircraft Corporation; page 73 (top), Wide World Photo; page 73 (bottom), Hiller Helicopters; pages 75 (top and bottom), 79, Bell Aircraft Corporation; pages 80, 81, International Harvester Company; pages 83, 84, 85, Hiller Helicopters; page 86, Bristol Aeroplane Company, Ltd.; page 89, British Information Services; page 90, Bristol Aeroplane Company, Ltd.; page 92 (top), British Information Services; page 92 (bottom), U.S. Air Force Photo; page 93, British Information Services; page 94, Helicopter Council; page 95, International News Photos; page 97 (top), Helicopter Council; pages 97 (bottom), 98, 99, 100, Port of New York Authority; page 102 (top), Bell Aircraft Corporation; page 102 (bottom), Hiller Helicopters; page 105 (top), Official U.S. Navy Photo; pages 105 (bottom), 106, 107, 108 (top), Department of Defense, U.S. Marine Corps Photos; pages 108 (bottom), 109 (top), U.S. Army Photos; page 109 (bottom), Department of Defense, U.S. Marine Corps Photo; page 110, U.S. Army Photo; page 111, Official U.S. Navy Photo; page 112 (top), Department of Defense, U.S. Marine Corps Photo; page 112 (bottom), U.S. Air Force Photo; page 113 (top), Department of Defense Photo; page 113 (bottom), U.S. Navy Photo; page 114, U.S. Air Force Photo; pages 115, 116 (top), Department of Defense, U.S. Marine Corps Photo; page 116 (bottom), Hiller Helicopters; page 117, U.S. Navy Photo; page 118 (top), U.S. Air Force Photo; page 118 (bottom), U.S. Army Photo; page 120 (top and bottom), International News Photos; page 121, National Film Board of Canada; Chapter 11, figures 1, 2, 5, 6, 7, 8, 9, 10, 11, 12, 13, 16, 17, Office of the Chief of Naval Operations, figures 14, 15, 18, Bell Aircraft Corporation; page 135 (fig. 1), Bell Aircraft Corporation, (fig. 2), Sikorsky Aircraft; page 136 (fig. 3), Bell Aircraft Corporation, (fig. 4), Kaman Aircraft Corporation; page 137 (fig. 5), Hiller Helicopters, (fig. 6), Office of the Chief of Naval Operations; page 139 (fig. 7), Gyrodyne Company, (fig. 8), Piasecki Helicopter Corporation, (fig. 9), Kaman Aircraft Corporation, (fig. 10), McCulloch Aircraft; page 140 (fig. 11), Piasecki Helicopter Corporation, (fig. 12), American Helicopter Co.; page 146, U.S. Army Photo; page 147, Bell Aircraft Corporation; page 149, Sikorsky Aircraft; pages 150 (top and bottom), 151 (top and bottom), 152 (top), British Information Services; page 152 (bottom), Glenview Metal Products Company; page 153 (top), Bristol Aeroplane Company, Ltd.; pages 153 (bottom), 154 (top), Convertawings, Inc.; page 154 (center), McDonnell Aircraft Corporation; pages 154 (bottom), 155 (top, center, and bottom), British Information Services; page 156, Piasecki Helicopter Corporation; page 158, Department of Defense Photo; page 159, U.S. Marine Photo.

1

THE FIRST REAL FLYING MACHINE

THE FIRST *REAL* FLYING MA-
chine—that's what some people call a helicopter.

Of course, other kinds of aircraft lift you off the ground. But is that flying? Not to a helicopter man. He will tell you that his machine is the only one that truly makes itself at home in the air.

To begin with, a copter flies in any direction. It can go straight up and straight down again, forward and backward and sideways. It stops and hovers in mid-air. It creeps along only a few inches above the ground. Then it climbs at an angle and speeds away, making a hundred miles an hour or better. Only one bird, the hummingbird, can compare with it.

This is the kind of flight men dreamed of through all the hundreds of years before they actually got off the ground. But, until helicopters came along, we had to be satisfied with flying in just one direction and two dimensions— forward and up, or forward and down. Now, at last, the helicopter adds other directions and a third dimension. And so we can call it the first *real* flying machine.

"First" is a word that you'll find a good many times in this book. That's because helicopters have just begun to make a place for themselves in the world. You are lucky enough to be in at the beginning of a great new time— the way people were a few years after the Wright brothers made their first flight at Kitty Hawk. Almost every day is a Kitty Hawk day for copters.

HALF BIRD AND HALF HORSE

A copter performs like a bird—but it's also as practical and hard-working as a horse. It can take you to places you couldn't reach in any other way, even

11

on horseback. Hopping from one rim of a deep canyon to another, it lands in a space not much bigger than itself. It can even stop and let you climb out on top of a sharp peak—or on the tip of a flagpole. Helicopters have jumped in and out of thick jungles or treacherous swamps. They have hoisted cargo over the trees through roadless wilderness.

When bad weather keeps airplanes grounded, copter pilots often go on about their business. They skim along underneath a blanket of cloud. "We fly when even the birds are walking," says one pilot. If he runs into a fog, he sets his machine down, gets out and scouts on foot to be sure nothing is in the way, then flies ahead and scouts some more—till he reaches home safely. He doesn't recommend it, of course, but he and many another pilot have done the trick in emergencies.

A copter is never bothered by traffic snarls, either. It lands on and takes off from small heliports on rooftops in the hearts of busy cities. And even if its engine conks out in the air, the pilot can almost always land safely, because the great whirling rotor blades keep turning as the copter falls. A skillful pilot can use this whirling action (it's called autorotation) to get himself down without a crash.

The rotor blades, of course, set the helicopter apart from any other kind of aircraft. Although they look like a huge propeller stuck on top of the fuselage, they really aren't. The blades are, in fact, wings. Rotary-wing aircraft—or just rotocraft—is another name for copters.

Unlike the fixed wings of airplanes, rotary wings have a double job to do. They provide lift for getting and staying off the ground, and they give the machine motion in all directions. That's a big order to fill. Later in the book we'll see exactly how they do it. Meantime let's take a look at the fascinating ancestors of these newest flying machines which people have affectionately nicknamed pinwheels, whirlybirds, choppers and eggbeaters.

THE MARVELOUS TOP

Our story begins about a hundred and fifty years ago when a sailing ship came back from the Orient, bringing silk and spices and a Chinese toy for a child in France. Nobody knows the exact date, or who the child was. But the toy, called a Chinese flying top, made history.

Somehow, somewhere, the French naturalist Launoy saw the top. As he examined the simple little gadget made of wood and string and feathers, he realized its marvelous possibilities. Here was a brand-new kind of flying machine. He wanted one for himself.

Launoy must not have been very handy with tools, for he asked a mechanic to whittle his toy and put it together. Then, one day in 1783, he took it to a meeting of the French Academy of Sciences. Bienvenu, the mechanic, went along.

Launoy's top set men to thinking of machines that would fly under their own power.

You can imagine the members of the Academy, dressed in knee breeches, lace cuffs and powdered wigs, watching politely while Bienvenu wound up the top. First he twisted it, so that the string wound round and round the upright stick. The ends of the string were attached to a little bow. The more Bienvenu wound the string up, the more taut he drew the bow. Now he was ready to let it go. The bow shot the top into the air above the astonished and fascinated scientists. Its feather blades whirled round and carried it away in flight.

Perhaps it seems strange for a group of dignified gentlemen in the eighteenth century to get excited about a flying top. But there was a reason for their interest. This was a special time in the history of the world. Modern science and industry had begun to grow. New ideas, experiments, and inventions were bubbling in many people's minds. Many other people were eager to get and use the new things that could be created. Benjamin Franklin had already flown his famous kite. Before long, electricity, steamships, railroads would be at work. Launoy, the scientist, and Bienvenu, the builder, were part of this lively, developing time.

Their Chinese top sailed over the heads of Frenchmen who had already grown air-minded. The world's first successful balloon flights were being made.

13

But, until Launoy showed off the top, his fellow-scientists had never before seen a heavier-than-air craft leave the ground under its own power. True, the winged top was only a model. But nobody doubted that real flying machines would come next. Thinkers had already begun to figure out some of the important principles of aeronautical science. No wonder the whirling feather blades fascinated everyone who saw them.

WHIRLING BLADES

Long before this, in the early 1500's, another air-minded inventor had thought about a whirling-blade machine. He drew pictures of it and even made some models. He was Leonardo da Vinci, the first real aviation scientist. The blade Leonardo designed was shaped like a screw. He figured out correctly that an air-screw should be able to pull a machine through the air, just as a wood screw pulls itself through wood. To describe his blade he used the Greek words *helix*, meaning spiral, and *pteron*, meaning wing. And that's how the name helicopter got started.

We don't know for sure whether any of Leonardo's models actually flew. Some people say they did. At any rate, he certainly understood a great deal about flight. Although most people forgot about his models for a long time, the things he wrote in his scientific notebooks helped later experimenters. In the end Leonardo realized that men would have to invent the right kind of engine before they could get real flying machines off the ground.

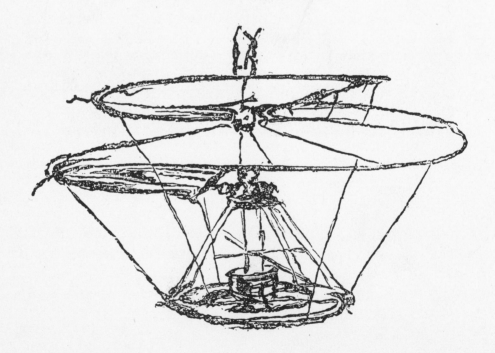

In 1500 da Vinci sketched this machine and called it helixpteron . . . or helicopter.

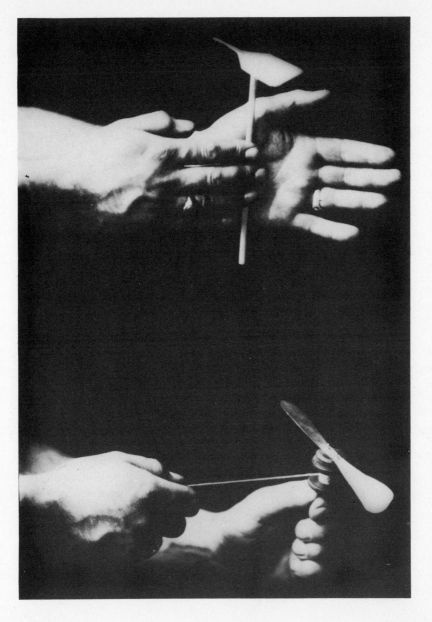

Cayley's top, launched by string wound on a spool, taught him the secret of flight.

An "engine" made of the bow-and-string winder lifted Launoy's top. Soon afterward an English schoolboy, George Cayley, saw the wonderful toy. He began to build flying models of his own. The top amused his friends, but it did more than that for young George. It made him wonder *why* the whirling blades soared into the air.

At last George had an improved model that rose ninety feet above the ground. Instead of using feathers in its wings, he cut blades from a sheet of tin and attached them to a stick. His "engine" for launching the top was a spool with a string wound around it. When George pulled the string, the spool revolved, spinning the blades very fast. Then up they went, climbing as they whirled.

But why? George kept on wondering.

Even after he left school he studied and experimented. His models showed him that a helicopter's wings had to be slightly tilted, so that the air pushed against them—the way it pushes against the underside of a flying kite. How could he use this same idea to make a machine that would carry a passenger aloft?

Finally, the whole secret of flight grew clear in George Cayley's mind. And he wrote it down in a few words that have been remembered by aircraft inventors from that day to this. You can make a flying machine work, said Cayley, by "the application of power to the resistance of the air."

In 1796, when he was twenty-three years old, Cayley drew detailed pictures of his top, and then he put the notebook away. Nobody had invented a good enough source of power for a real flying machine. But the helicopter idea kept working at the back of Cayley's mind. In 1843 he put a new idea on paper. Steam engines were now supplying power to drive ships and locomotives. Why shouldn't they drive an "aerial carriage?"

Cayley drew up plans for a full-size copter. The rotors—four of them—looked like enormous pinwheels. Belts were supposed to transmit power from a steam engine to the rotors, which would turn in opposite directions. This was more than sixty years before the first whirlybird actually left the ground, but already, students like Cayley knew how the rotors had to be turned.

The "aerial carriage" remained only a plan. Cayley probably suspected that any steam engine he could buy or build would be far too heavy for wings to lift. This was the really baffling thing to Cayley and all the other aeronauts. They knew they had reached the door to powered flight, but they couldn't step through. If only they could solve the engine problem!

Inventors were tantalized by the fact that model aircraft, equipped with tiny steam engines, had actually flown. Horatio Phillips built one in England. A Frenchman, Gustave d'Amecourt, built and flew some models. One of them had a parachute stuck like an umbrella on top. Then the Frenchman went to work on a full-scale copter which had a steam engine. The machine failed to fly, but it added still another step. D'Amecourt used aluminum for some of his engine parts, trying to lighten them.

By 1878, Enrico Forlanini had invented a truly remarkable tiny steam engine. He installed it in a model helicopter, and up it went—up to forty feet. The flight lasted twenty seconds. The engine was light and cleverly designed, but if Forlanini had built it full-size for a piloted helicopter, it wouldn't have been practical. It couldn't deliver continuous power for any length of time.

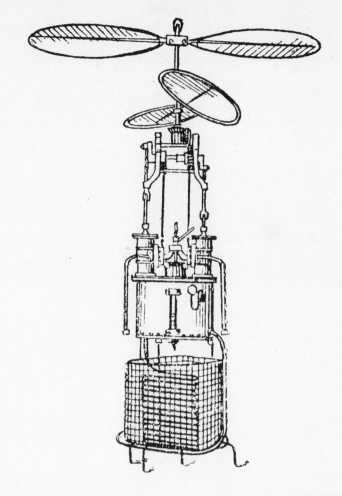

D'Amecourt built a steam engine to power his helicopter, but it failed to lift it.

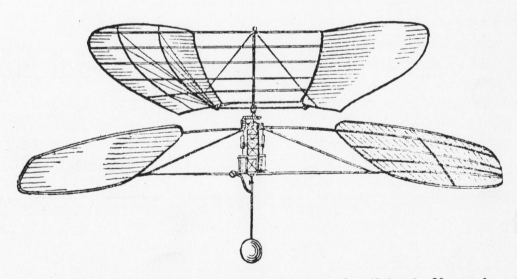

In 1878 Forlanini built a steam-driven model. It hovered at 40 feet for 20 seconds.

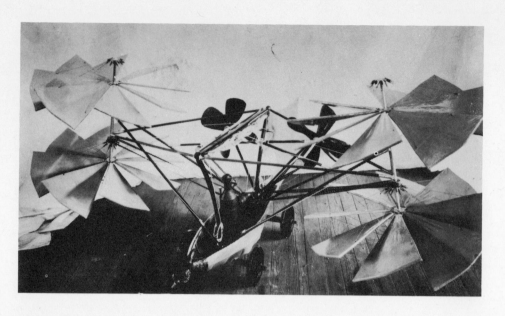

Cayley's 1843 model had four rotors. Problem was where to get power to turn them.

BRONCOS WITH WINGS

The search went on and on, until at last inventors came up with the kind of engine everybody needed—a gasoline engine. Meantime, two little boys in America had been playing with a Chinese flying top. Soon they dreamed up model helicopters of their own. The models convinced young Orville and Wilbur Wright that flying machines were the most important things on earth. They really studied wings and tried to find out what made them fly. They tinkered with all kinds of machinery and learned a great many practical things, too. Finally they decided they were ready to build a flying machine. But it wouldn't be a helicopter.

The practical Wrights had figured out that the mechanical difficulties with a helicopter would be stupendous. They liked solving problems, but first and foremost they wanted to fly.

Shortly after the Wrights flew their first plane, Charles Renard, a French scientist-inventor, built a little copter with two rotors and a gasoline engine. It flew by itself, but without a pilot. If he had gone on working, Renard might have succeeded in getting a ride in it. Instead, he merely gave lectures on the science of helicopters and concentrated on flying lighter-than-air craft.

One of Renard's students was Louis Breguet. By 1907, Breguet had built an odd-looking machine that was all square angles. It had four rotors constructed like the wings of a biplane, but no devices to control it in flight—no rudder for steering, nothing to help steady it in the air.

Just the same, Breguet climbed aboard one day and took off! His machine

Emile Berliner's helicopter flew, but he felt it was too unsafe to be practical.

Breguet's 1907 model lifted him five feet, but it pitched like a bucking bronco.

lifted him five feet above the ground. The first full-scale piloted helicopter had arrived. It wobbled and pitched like a bucking bronco. It was so uncontrollable that Breguet decided not even to bother trying to improve it. He went to work on a new type. When this one, too, failed, he gave up.

19

Cornu's version, with rotor blades like giant fly-swatters, lifted him a few feet.

At about this same time, another French inventor, Paul Cornu, finished a weird machine. It had two rotors, each with two blades which looked like giant fly swatters. Unlike Breguet, Cornu had installed a balancing device on his copter. But he didn't trust the thing. Before taking off, he tethered it to the ground so it couldn't run away with him. His caution wasn't really necessary. The rotors lifted him about five feet off the ground. That was all. His controls didn't control it, either. It pitched as badly as Breguet's machine. Cornu gave up in disgust.

But the story of his copter spread across Europe, and the next year an air-minded visitor from Russia came to France. Eighteen-year-old Igor Sikorsky called on Cornu, eagerly asking for information and a look at the discarded machine. All that winter Sikorsky stayed in France, learning what he could from the French aviation men. He had already made some experiments of his own with models and a four-foot blade rigged to a pulley. His enthusiasm had moved his school-teacher sister to give him all her savings for the trip to Paris.

When he returned to his home in Kiev, young Igor went to work in his father's garden, building a helicopter of his own. Although Frenchmen had talked to him mainly about fixed-wing craft, he determined to make his own experiments with whirling blades. He saw how useful it would be to jump right into the air with a helicopter, instead of using the long runway that air-planes needed.

Unlike Cornu's helicopter, Sikorsky's machine had rotors set one above the other. This, he felt, would make it more controllable. At last he was ready to try it. He could feel the wings working to get it off the ground. At the same time, they seemed to be trying to tip it over on its side. The inventor, however,

Bitten by the helicopter bug, Sikorsky built this model in Kiev, Russia, in 1910.

was not discouraged. With even greater enthusiasm, he began figuring how to take off some of the weight—and how to give greater stability.

A year later, the second helicopter was finished. This time it almost got into the air. But, for all his careful work and planning, Sikorsky knew that he had something like a rebellious horse on his hands. Even if he lightened the machine still more, he would need a different engine and better-designed wings.

Like the Wrights, Igor Sikorsky was a practical young man. He had spent far too much of his family's money already. A great many problems would have to be solved before inventors could give helicopters real stability and control in the air. He still wanted to fly, so he turned to the simpler business of fixed-wing aircraft. Perhaps experiments with airplanes would provide the knowledge he needed to build a successful helicopter.

Sikorsky was right. Many years later, after he had moved to the United States, he did develop a remarkable copter—the first successful one in America.

Meantime, other inventors kept on stubbornly experimenting. In 1908, an American, Emile Berliner, built a machine that he saw was too dangerous to be practical. That same year, J. C. H. Ellehammer built a copter in Denmark, but he never got more than four feet off the ground in it.

Ellehammer's copter had two superimposed airscrews rotating in opposite directions.

In 1916, two Austrians, Petroczy and von Karman, put together a machine that military men hoped would be very useful. They believed it could hover high in the air and serve as an observation post for watching enemy operations. The Austrian copter had three engines. Its two rotors whirled *underneath* the cabin where the observer and pilot sat. To avoid the problem of stability and control, the inventors harnessed it with cables, so that it merely went up and down like a captive balloon. Before it finally crashed, it made several flights up to nearly a hundred feet, and it stayed up an hour at a time.

After the First World War, Emile Berliner and his son, Henry, went to work again. They produced two models, one in 1920 and another in 1924. The first of these machines consisted of a small, heavy framework which served both as an engine mount and support for the co-axial rotors they used. With this machine they attained a hovering height of about four feet. The second model had two rotors mounted on the tops of the right and left wings, and while it was stable enough to fly forward pretty well, it wasn't nearly safe enough to be useful.

FROM OCTOPUS TO EGGBEATER

American Army people had watched the Berliner machine on one of its flights, and it encouraged them to go ahead with one of the strangest of all helicopter experiments. They asked an aviation scientist, George de Bothezat, to build a military copter. By 1922 it was ready to fly. When the inventor brought his machine out of the shop where he had kept it hidden from almost everybody, the spectators gasped. It seemed to combine every outlandish feature of all its ancestors, and it was simply enormous. Four huge rotors were

22

Berliner's son, Henry, designed this machine that flew with some success in 1924.

De Bothezat's copter, called "Flying Octopus," was too hard to fly to be useful.

mounted at the ends of a fuselage built in the shape of a cross. Four other "fans" served as controls to guide and stabilize the ship, which was immediately called the "Flying Octopus." But contrary to everybody's fears, the monstrosity flew. Not only that, it was fairly stable.

The military men watched it perform about a hundred flights. Then they said no. The de Bothezat copter was too hard to fly, too complicated. It couldn't compete with fixed-wing craft.

Still experiments went on. Pateras de Pescara in Spain built several helicopters that flew, and Etienne Oehmichen built a peculiar blimp-helicopter in France. In 1924, Oehmichen built a second craft that made record flights. It rivalled de Bothezat's in complexity. It had four rotors for lift, and five auxiliary propellers for control, another propeller for steering, and two airplane-type propellers to give forward speed. In all, there were thirteen transmissions to take power from the engine!

This was just about the last of the weird contraptions. From then on, helicopters could be simpler, thanks to a discovery made by the Spanish inventor, Juan de la Cierva.

THE AUTOGYRO

In the beginning, Cierva built ordinary fixed-wing aircraft. Then he began to wonder what would happen if he made a sort of hybrid machine—a cross between a helicopter and an airplane.

Spain was not without its helicopter experiments. Pescara built this one in 1924.

Pescara's coaxial-type helicopter was very complicated, but it flew nevertheless.

Oehmichen's 1924 model had four rotors, five propellers, and it set flight records.

Oehmichen's copter did not have enough power to fly, so he added a balloon to it.

Cierva called his craft an "autogyro." It was an ordinary small airplane with a set of whirling blades on top. The fixed wings and the regular propeller lifted the autogyro off the ground. But, once it was going, the motion of the air past the rotary wings kept them whirling, although they were not connected with the engine. This was called "autorotation." With no extra help from the engine, the whirling wings gave the plane extra lift.

This meant that the autogyro could fly more slowly than an ordinary plane if necessary. It could rise much more quickly at the take-off. In fact, it could almost jump into the air. Of course, it couldn't hover like a true helicopter, because the blades were not turned by the engine. They stopped when the plane stopped moving.

Before Cierva perfected his autogyro, he made some mistakes. And in correcting them he discovered one of the rules for a workable helicopter. The blades needed to have a certain amount of flexibility.

Cierva's first rotor blades were rigid. As soon as they began to whirl around with the forward motion of the plane, the whole thing tipped over on its side. The same thing happened with three different experimental machines.

The inventor was puzzled. He built a model autogyro with rotor blades made of flexible stuff called rattan. The model did not tip over. At last the answer to the problem dawned on Cierva. Rotary wings had to be flexible.

Key to successful rotary-wing flight came from Cierva's development of the autogyro.

Cierva put hinges on the blades of his next autogyro. This fourth one took to the air in 1923 without a hitch.

The autogyro, first cousin to the helicopter, has now disappeared from the sky. But thanks to Cierva's brilliant experiments, the true whirlybird's inventors had a much easier task.

UP AND AWAY!

By 1930, a Dutch inventor, A. G. von Baumhauer, had thought of a new idea. He built a copter with a single main rotor and a smaller rotor in the tail The experts kept telling him that the tail rotor wouldn't work. But when he took off, it did.

At about the same time, Corridino d'Ascanio made record flights in Italy. His copter, with two main rotors and three small propellers, could travel for more than half a mile straight ahead; it could truly hover about twenty feet above the earth; and it stayed aloft for nearly nine minutes.

Louis Breguet, who had given up helicopters in 1907, began to think about them again. In 1934 he built a whirlybird that had real stability and control. Although it was too heavy for long flights, many people think it should be called the world's first completely successful helicopter.

Others think the honor should go to Heinrich Focke, a German inventor.

27

Breguet's 1934 machine is considered by many to have been first successful copter.

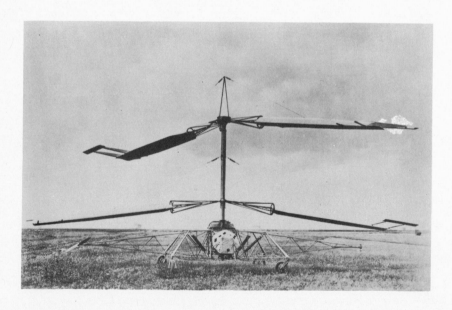

D'Ascanio added three small auxiliary propellers to his machine to secure control.

D'Ascanio's copter, with two main rotors, three small ones, stayed up 9 minutes.

In 1937, his copter, called the Focke-Achgelis FW-61, did indeed set new records: a flight of 1 hour, 20 minutes; speed of 76 miles per hour; distance, 143 miles; altitude, 11,243 feet. The FW-61 could hover, go straight up and down, forward and backward—all with excellent stability and control.

Rotary wings, the first to lift a model aircraft, were the last to carry their inventors aloft.

The Focke-Achgelis set new records in 1937. It flew for one hour and 20 minute

2

HOW THE EGGBEATERS
WERE HATCHED

IGOR SIKORSKY WAS A PRAC-
tical dreamer. His first helicopter failed to lift him out of his father's garden,
so he abandoned it. But for thirty years he studied the experiments of others,
and at last he decided to try again.

By 1939, Sikorsky had become a successful designer and manufacturer of
airplanes, with a big factory in Connecticut. In one corner of the factory he
began to work on a new helicopter which he called the VS 300. Other people
in the plant teased him a little and called his invention "Igor's nightmare."
But, one day in September, he was ready to test the VS 300. It flew.

Just to be on the safe side, Sikorsky used ropes on a ball and chain to hold
the copter down to an altitude of a few feet during the early tests. The
tethered VS 300 taught its inventor a great many things about the preculiar
behavior of rotary wings. And, of course, he had to teach himself how to fly it.
This was no easy job. The copter vibrated so much that people on the ground
said it looked like one big blur in the air.

Time and again Sikorsky took the VS 300 apart, put it together with im-
provements and tested once more—always with the machine tethered. Finally,
in May 1940, he was ready to set it free.

This time he let some outsiders watch the flight, in addition to the men who
had been working with him at the plant. They were enchanted with the per-
formance he put on—flying straight up and down, backward and sideward,
hovering, turning round and round and in mid-air. Everyone was so interested
in the tricks he performed that they didn't even notice one important thing:

30

In 1939, Igor Sikorsky ran tests for rotor study in open field next to factory.

Sikorsky's VS-300 brought endurance record to U.S. It flew one hour, 32 minutes.

31

An early Sikorsky experiment, flying in 1941, used second rotor near tail rotor.

the VS 300 scarcely flew forward at all. The fact was, it couldn't fly forward very well!

Sikorsky listened to the congratulations with his tongue in his cheek. Then he went back to work. Later on he explained gently that forward flight was just a minor problem he hadn't yet solved. He wasn't really joking, either. During the next year he solved it—and a lot of other problems, too. He wanted to make his rebuilt copter as precise as the hummingbird itself.

Meantime, the United States Army had again become interested in helicopters, and Sikorsky was asked to build an experimental military craft. In 1942 it was ready—the XR-4, twice as big and powerful as the VS 300. Sikorsky decided to give the Army observers a little fun as they watched the XR-4 make its exhibition flight. The test pilot took off with a net bag full of eggs fastened by a rope to the copter. Up he went, then down again, and set the eggs on the ground as gently as if he were a housewife, with not one broken.

At this point, one of Sikorsky's engineers heard someone mutter, "I bet they're hardboiled." Without a word he marched over and flung a couple of the eggs down on the ground. Their splash silenced the doubter.

THE "FLYING BANANA"

The Second World War had started military men on the search for new

32

Wearing inflated life jacket, Igor Sikorsky hovers early model VS-300 over water.

kinds of aircraft. Helicopters seemed to offer great possibilities for lifesaving and rescue work. And so the government decided to spend a lot of money encouraging inventors to perfect rotary-wing craft. Money was what they needed. A helicopter cost so much to produce that most people could not get beyond building one experimental machine. But, with large amounts of government help, inventors could make one new improvement after another.

While Sikorsky was developing the VS 300, young Frank Piasecki began to dream of building a copter of his own. With four friends, he started to work in an old store in Philadelphia. Some of their material came from a railroad junk yard. They borrowed money from Frank's father and managed to squeak along till they finished a neat little machine with a single main rotor and small tail rotor. The ship took off from a farmer's field one day in 1943. But already its builders had started to plan something bigger—and completely different. With a government contract, they designed and constructed a helicopter that could only have been nicknamed the "Flying Banana."

This odd-looking long, thin craft had two rotors, one at each end—an arrangement called tandem-rotor. It was not beautiful, but it was sturdy. Piasecki knew he was on the right track, aiming toward big machines that could haul big loads. In the ten years that followed his first flight, he worked up to a military transport that carried forty passengers. With very little change, it could be made into a sky bus that would operate on regular schedules between cities.

33

First Sikorsky Army helicopter was the XR-4, almost twice the size of the VS-300.

To show VS-300's hovering stability, pilot noses copter against up-raised hand.

34

Meantime, eighteen-year-old Stanley Hiller, Jr., built his first copter and flew it in 1943. It had two rotors, with the axle of one built inside the axle of the other. Both were turned by the same engine. (This is called a co-axial type.) Five years later he perfected a quite different machine with a single main rotor and a small tail rotor. And then came a little ship which he called the *Hornet*— completely unlike any of the others.

The *Hornet* was revolutionary for several reasons. First, it could be made to sell for a very low price. It could be parked in an ordinary garage. It was easy to pilot. It was "the least complicated piece of flying machinery yet built," according to one expert.

The secret behind all this was the kind of engine that Hiller gave the *Hornet*. Most helicopters get their power from an airplane-type engine mounted in the fuselage. Through a system of gears, the engine turns the rotors. No matter how good this kind of power plant is, it has one disadvantage. It develops something that engineers call "torque." On page 129 you can find out exactly what happens because of torque. Just this: If you have one main rotor that whirls from left to right, you will find the body of your copter whirling from right to left as soon as you get into the air. You will, that is, unless you think up some device for solving the problem.

Sikorsky and others solved it by putting a small rotor in the tail of the machine. This little rotor keeps pushing sideways all the time and holds the copter's body steady. Piasecki did the trick by using two main rotors. One cancels out the torque of the other.

Tiny tip-mounted jet units that power Hiller Hornet weigh only 12 pounds each.

All of these devices require heavy parts—gear boxes, extra rotors, extra length. But when Stanley Hiller built the *Hornet*, he got rid of such things by getting rid of torque altogether. Instead of using one big engine in the fuselage, he used two little jet engines—one at the tip of each rotor blade.

In the beginning, Hiller wanted to build his small jet *Hornets* by the thousand, so that private pilots could own and fly them. But a government contract persuaded him to work on military jet copters instead. Some people in California will tell you now that the things called "flying saucers" are really Hiller's experimental machines. The flame-spitting jets whirl so fast through the night sky that they might be taken for ships from Mars.

WHIRLYBIRDS AT WORK

Back in the days when Stanley Hiller was still in school, Arthur Young began to experiment with ideas for a single-rotor helicopter. Then he joined the Bell Aircraft Corporation and went on working out plans. By 1946 the Bell Model 47 received the first commercial helicopter license ever granted in the United States. This meant that government experts thought the copter was a

Hiller test pilot lights one of the ram-jet engines that power the little Hornet.

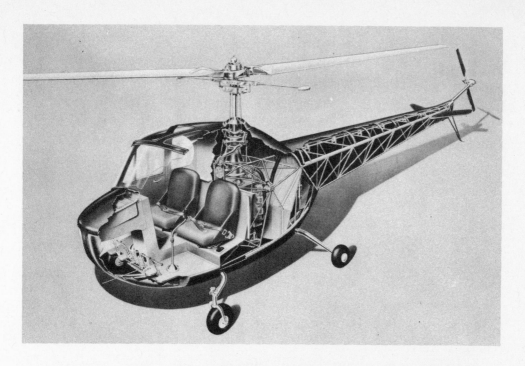

Cutaway shows cyclic pitch stick in front of seat; collective pitch, left of seat.

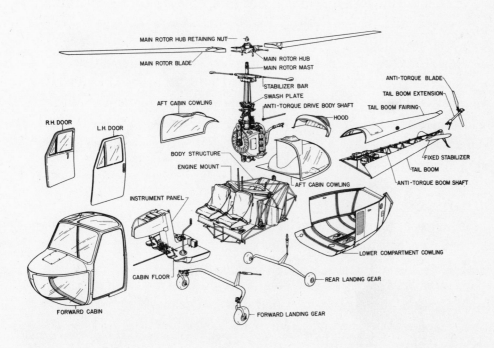

Breakaway drawing of a Bell 47 details helicopter's components and construction.

Powered by a gas turbine, the Kaman K-225 is in process of development for Navy.

good, safe machine for ordinary citizens to fly. Since then, Bell has built military models, but the company's main interest was in selling copters for workaday use.

At first, this wasn't an easy job. People had to be convinced that the whirlybird could do certain jobs well. But gradually the idea took hold. Word spread around that copters were better than other machines for some kinds of work, such as spraying and dusting fields, or scouting over forest fires. There were even a few jobs that only a copter could do. (What else could actually deliver Santa Claus to a rooftop?)

BIG ONES AND LITTLE ONES

Like seeds in the springtime, helicopter ideas sprouted by the dozen. A few of them actually grew into good-sized plants, but many of them have been weeded out.

For instance, a young engineer named Glidden Doman designed and built the first ship in this country that had four blades on its single main rotor. In 1953, Stanley Hiller acquired the rights to produce the military version of Glidden Doman's machine.

Charles H. Kaman built a ship with intermeshing rotors. That means he

Using intermeshing rotors, the Kaman HOK-1 is a utility helicopter for Navy use.

Youthful engineer-designer Doman's copter has four blades on its single rotor.

placed two main rotors side by side, both turned by the same engine. In order to keep the blades from bumping into each other, he geared them to turn the way an eggbeater's blades turn.

Another interesting copter was the McCulloch MC-4. It had tandem rotors like the "Flying Banana," but was much smaller. The Gyrodyne also had two rotors, but they were co-axial—one above the other. A Kellet model was equipped with two engines to turn its two big rotors. A small jet machine, called "Little Henry," built by the McDonnell Aircraft Corporation of St. Louis, Missouri, performed somewhat like the Hiller *Hornet*.

Howard Hughes built a monstrous jet craft with rotor blades 136 feet from tip to tip. It was designed to work like a flying crane which would lift enormous weights and carry them for short distances.

And at the other end of the scale was a Rotor-Craft model—nothing but a set of personal whirling wings attached by a harness to the pilot's body!

It is hard to tell what will become of all these ingenious ideas. Some of them may be abandoned. Others are still being tested. At any rate, the hatching of ideas still goes on.

ALL KINDS OF GEAR

While some men were inventing new rotorcraft, others were putting their minds to helicopter equipment. In addition to landing wheels, whirlybirds

Another possibility for short-haul trips is the five-passenger coaxial GCA 2C.

Hughes Aircraft's giant jet XH-17 is designed to carry over 12 tons some 65 miles.

Even this set of personal whirlywings

had its beginning in a Chinese toy.

McCulloch MC-4, like the Piasecki "Flying Banana," is a tandem-rotor helicopter.

Brantly B-2 carries pilot, a passenger. Tail caster protects tail rotor on ground.

Enemy subs will have little chance if they are spotted by the Navy's Bell HSL-1.

Navy's HTK-1 or Civil K-240 is three-place machine that can be used as ambulance.

Navy men practice climbing aboard "Flying Banana" for air-sea rescue.

now have pontoons or flotation gear for use on water or marshy ground. Since the pilot can set a copter down with a soft plunk anywhere, the pontoons are just as good for landing on a rooftop as on water. Even the big Piaseckis have doughnut-shaped flotation gear. These pontoons fit around the wheels and can be blown up when they are needed. For rough country or for landings on snow, Bell copters and others have landing skids that look like skis.

Hauling people out of dangerous places was one of the helicopter's first jobs. And so rescue hoists had to be invented—cables that could be lowered and raised, and a harness to fit around the body of the rescued person. Coast Guard and military copters have this equipment, of course. But commercial pilots have done so many emergency lifesaving jobs that they always carry a length of rope in the cockpit—just in case.

BETTER PINWHEELS

While all this specialized equipment was being invented, people kept busy at Igor Sikorsky's factory in Connecticut, too. They designed and built new and better models for both civilian and military uses. Big S-55's began to carry mail on a regular schedule in and out of Los Angeles, for example. In 1952, a pair of Sikorsky H-19's were the first helicopters to cross the Atlantic Ocean.

44

The Air Force Piasecki YH-16 "Transporter" can carry 40 passengers, crew of three.

Equipped with flotation gear, a Coast Guard chopper lands to check a small boat.

Today, 12 years after the X-4, fleets of Sikorskys are flown in scheduled service.

Today it gives you a queer feeling to stand outside the Sikorsky plant, watching the test pilots at work. You remember that less than fifteen years ago, Igor Sikorsky himself didn't even know how to fly his whirlybird. He was his own first test pilot. Every time he made a change in a model, he had to feel out the results of what he'd done to the machine. Only when he was quite sure that his copter wouldn't commit murder did he train other pilots to fly it and test it.

Nowadays things are quite different. After a new copter has been assembled, it goes out onto the field and a test pilot climbs aboard. In a few minutes the machine is performing like a cross between a bronco and an angry bumblebee. It bucks. It zooms up, down, backwards. A perfectly confident pilot is simply giving it the works—to make sure that one more whirlybird is in perfect condition before it is delivered.

All over the world pioneer pilots in every type of helicopter have begun to unwind a fascinating story of experience and adventure. They have already proved that no other machine keeps man so close to the ground—and yet so free from all the limitations of movement on the earth. In the words of Igor Sikorsky, "A helicopter is the most universal vehicle yet created by man."

That's a lot to believe. So—let's have a look at what helicopters have done and can do.

3

WILDERNESS WORK

THE FOREST RANGER STARED
down at the trees. Two plumes of smoke, a big one and a little one, showed
where lightning had started a fire in the great lonely Canadian woods. A shiver
went up the ranger's spine, but not for the usual reasons. This fire was going
to be different. He intended to fight it in a new way—with a helicopter, the
very helicopter that was carrying him toward the smoke at that very moment.

Al Souter, pilot of the Bell 47D, glanced at the ranger and knew exactly
how he felt. A man is just naturally tense before he gets used to sitting in an
open-type helicopter cockpit with the rotor buzzing overhead. The clear plastic
shield in front looks like nothing at all, and you have the odd feeling that even
the seat beneath you is just a cushion of air. It's hard at first to believe how
trustworthy a whirlybird really is.

The ranger leaned against the safety belt as the copter turned and came in
closer. How big was the fire? Which way was it spreading—through what kind
of wood? Before long he found out. Souter took him down and hovered thirty
feet above the trees. For the first time in history, a Canadian forester sat still
over a blaze and noted everything on his map. Of course, the pilot had to be
careful. A fire sends up hot gases that push a lot of air away. If the copter's
engine doesn't get enough oxygen, it conks out. Usually a pilot knows by the
look of the air whether it's safe. A bluish gray cast means he'd better clear out.

A few quick notes on the map, then Souter and the ranger were off to scout
over the surrounding territory. Roadless wilderness stretched out as far as they
could see in every direction. The nearest source of men and fire-fighting equipment was sixty miles away. Fifteen miles from the blaze, they sighted a clear

47

Trucks can't make the climb, but the copter can in the mountainous Canadian wilds.

stretch of water—Livermore Lake. And just below them, less than four hundred yards from the fire, lay a waterhole, not a very big one, but Souter thought it would do. He could ease his pontoon-equipped machine down for a landing there.

Briskly they worked out their strategy, then radioed to headquarters. A seaplane loaded with men and tools must take off immediately for Livermore Lake. From the lake, Souter would taxi the load to the waterhole which was big enough for the helicopter but far too small a landing spot for an airplane. While the two men were waiting for the fire crew to arrive, they would clear away trees, enlarging the space around the waterhole so the crew could get ashore. It was all just as simple as that.

Inside of three hours the whole crew, with their tools and water pumps, were on the fire line, hard at work.

48

Maybe three hours sounds like a long time to get action after the alarm has been turned in. But you won't think so once you've seen what the forests in Canada and northern United States are like. These great areas of wilderness have few roads. In many places there are no roads at all, not even a trail for men to follow on foot. Crews must literally hack their way through the bush before they reach the place where they start to fight the fire. Bushwhacking, they call it, and it's exhausting work. By the time they reach the blaze they're too dead tired to do a top job of fire-fighting.

Remember, fifteen miles of wilderness lay between Livermore Lake and the waterhole where Al Souter set his copter down. It would have taken thirty-six hours to chop a trail that far through the bush! The portable water pumps weighed 135 pounds apiece, and no pack animals were available, except the human animal. Meanwhile the fire would have been crackling away unchecked, eating up more and more acres of forest.

With the copter for a taxi, Souter ferried men and tools in four-hundred-pound loads across that strip of dense wilderness between the lake and the waterhole. At first they tried carrying the bulky water pumps on the seat in the cockpit. Later, they worked out a way of hauling the equipment strapped to small platforms above the pontoons. And nobody got overtired, not even Souter himself, a pioneer if there ever was one.

"A MIRACLE"

You can see why old-timers in forest-fire control think that three hours instead of thirty-six is something of a miracle. "After twenty-five years, I have seen what I dreamed of," one of them says. "A service that gets me what I need there right now." He has seen helicopters at work in the state of Washington, and he, too, can measure in hours instead of days the time it takes to get fresh, unwearied men on the fire line.

There's even faster action when helicopters operate in the Angeles Forest of Southern California. This is different country—a country of deep canyons with steep slopes, rocky peaks, lots of low brush. All these make fire-fighting difficult. Although roads lead into the forest from towns and cities nearby, it used to take as much as forty hours for men to scout a fire area by auto and on foot. A helicopter carries the fire boss on the same reconnoitering trip in sixty minutes.

The first time whirlybirds answered the alarm in Angeles Forest was back in August 1947. The fire had started at the bottom of a canyon and was spreading upward along both steep slopes. Two helicopter pilots, Knute Flint and Fred Bowen, went to work and stayed on the job four days. They fought gusts of wind as well as smoke, and the temperature hit 107 degrees.

Fighting gusts of wind, smoke and heat, U.S. Forest Service copter scouts the area.

On many fires the Forest Service can call out its mechanized equipment—bulldozers, tank trucks and the like. But this one started climbing up hillsides too steep for machines. It had to be handled by men with only the tools they could carry. Flint and Bowen undertook to set them down at the spots where they were needed most.

In some places a man could heave his axe overboard, then swing himself down from the copter and chop an emergency heliport out of the brush. On the next trips the pilot could land there and let reinforcements off. But there was one peak in the fire zone that had no landing spot worth mentioning. A patch of rocks eight feet long and eight feet wide offered the only visible touchdown area. And there the copter landed safely—with only three of its four wheels on terra firma!

In the four days that the fire lasted, Flint and Bowen taxied almost three hundred men to places where they were desperately needed. In addition, they carried the fire bosses on scores of trips to map the fire, scout for unexpected trouble, and plan the method of fighting. A good many men were injured or knocked out by heat and exhaustion. Then the copters did ambulance duty, carrying more than a dozen serious cases for medical treatment.

Most important of all, the whirlybirds did something for the spirits of the

Firefighting whirlybirds stop to refuel during Wheeler Springs forest blaze in California.

men who worked at the fearfully dangerous jobs on the fire line. A machine that can hover and pick you out of a tight spot gives you confidence. You spend more energy fighting and less of it worrying, if you know you're only helicopter minutes—not hours—from a doctor. On a job that lasts for days, men need food, bedding, water to drink. All these an eggbeater can bring in. If there's one thing that cheers up a weary, singed fire-fighter, it's ice cream. That, too, is on the cargo list.

Ever since that historic experiment, helicopters have done regular fire duty in the Angeles Forest and in other West Coast forests, too.

Things that were novelties once have become routine. Hot meals, for instance. A copter can pick up food that has been prepared at the fire camp, or even in a restaurant. Dinner for a dozen men—beef in gravy, mashed potatoes, green beans, coffee—goes into four or five pots which fit together in one big "hot can." Then the giant thermos bottle can be ferried quickly to the top of a mountain or the bottom of a canyon.

After a forest fire has been put out, everybody wants to go home. The excitement is over, and dog-tired men would almost rather go on working than shoulder their tools and start the long walk back along the trail. With a helicopter available, they don't have to. "Eggbeating is much preferred to leg-

51

Injured fire-fighter is lifted from copter that brought him out of danger area.

beating," one fire dispatcher says. The taxi-home service isn't offered entirely because fire officers are softhearted. They find that volunteer fire-fighters are easier to recruit if the men know they won't have to spend a day or two or three walking home.

TRICKS OF THE TRADE

Pilots and fire officers have now worked out so many problems together that they have regular routines which don't even seem exciting—to them. But once in a while something unusual happens. One common trick, for instance, is the old practice of fighting fire with fire. This was developed long before helicopters came on the scene, and it's called backfiring. After the boss has surveyed the problem, he orders the crew to start a new blaze, which they can control, right in the path of the big fire which has got out of hand. The new fire eats up fuel all along the line. Then the men put it out. By the time the big fire reaches the spot there's nothing left to burn, and the onrushing flames die down.

Usually the helicopter serves only as an observation platform in a backfiring operation. But at least once it took an active part in the job, by actually blowing a wind into the face of a fire, and holding it back until it burned itself out. The wind came from the copter's whirling rotor blades, which create a terrific downwash of air.

Another time the pilot was actually able to blow out the flames of a brush fire, just by using the downwash.

One of the oddest rescue jobs in the forest happened like this: The pilot glanced down at an open place surrounded by smoke and flames. Something moved in the underbrush. At first he thought it was a stranded fire-fighter. So he hovered for a minute, looked closer and saw a tiny deer, apparently alone and cut off from its mother. The pilot made a quick landing, grabbed the fawn and was off again, carrying a startled little passenger to safety.

In Canada, the rangers discovered still another practical job for the egg-beaters to do in places so wild that fire observation towers had not yet been built there. Offhand, you might say that it shouldn't be too hard a job to locate the best spot for a fire tower. Just stick it on top of the highest hill. But that's easier said than done. Even when you can fly over hilly, heavily-timbered country in an airplane, you can't always judge which hill will give you the best building place with the best view.

In the old days, the job of locating and building a tower was unbelievably slow and tedious. First an airplane flew over and scouted. Then material for a temporary tower was carried by plane to the nearest lake. Here construction workers began bushwhacking toward the chosen hill. After they had chopped out a trail, they had to tote the material, piece by piece, and set the tower up. There was a fifty-fifty chance that this was the right spot on a high enough hill. But two times out of four it wasn't. So the exasperated men had to tear the structure down and bushwhack it to a better place or a higher hill. Only when they found the right combination was material for the permanent tower ferried in and set up. You can see why it took a good summer's work to locate building sites for ten towers in this way.

Now a forest ranger goes out in a helicopter. He has a map, and he's a pretty good judge of trees. While the pilot hovers low over the forest, the ranger can tell by careful inspection just about how tall the trees on this hill are. He then imagines that the seat of the helicopter is the platform of an observation tower. Still hovering, the pilot swings the copter around in a full circle, without moving up, down or sideways. The ranger sights in all directions. In a short time he can try out all the possible places in the area, and when he's finished he knows just where the tower should be built and how tall it must be. No trial and error, no costly and aggravating temporary structure.

Instead of locating spots for ten fire observation towers in a whole summer, the copter-borne ranger can locate seven in one day!

After the fire, things must grow again, so the helicopter sows mustard seeds.

PLANTING NEW FORESTS

Every extinguished fire brings still another problem to the Forest Service: the problem of soil and water conservation. The burned-over area must be covered with new growth as soon as possible. Plants and trees must be encouraged to send down roots which keep rains from washing away soil and causing floods. Again, there's a job for a helicopter.

First it goes out with load after load of poisoned bait to kill off hungry forest creatures that may be looking for a free meal. Next, the copter scatters seeds—mustard seed, which grows quickly, to hold back soil erosion, and sometimes the seeds of Ponderosa pine or other evergreen trees to start new forests among the blackened ruins of the old. Helicopters have speeded up reforestation in burned areas as large as 10,000 acres, and they finish the task in record time.

When projects of this sort were first started, men on foot sowed the seeds. It took ten days for a twelve-man crew to cover a thousand acres. Then the Forest Service (with lumber companies co-operating) tried airplanes. A plane speeds up the job, but it has its drawbacks. For one thing, it must fly so high and so fast that the seeds cannot always be distributed evenly. And it can't reach the very steep slopes where erosion is likely to be worst. That's because tricky, unpredictable air currents circulate around mountain sides. A whole crew of men is needed on the ground, too. They set up markers which keep the airplane pilot on his course. They signal him if the seeds are falling too

Mustard seed, now in flower, was sown by helicopter to hold back soil erosion.

thickly or in too thin a stream. They wave him back to places he has missed entirely. And hillsides still have to be sown by men on foot.

A helicopter, on the other hand, can fly safely along at a slow, even speed, fairly close to the ground. The pilot can check for himself and see that every acre has been properly covered. He can control his machine in gusty air that might wreck a plane, and so steep banks and hillsides give him little trouble. In one day a copter can re-seed exactly the same area that it once took ten days for twelve men to cover on foot.

ODD JOBS

Another government agency uses a copter for planting jobs, too. The Fish and Wildlife Service actually sows fish from the air! For years the state and national governments have re-stocked streams and lakes with baby fish raised in hatcheries, so that anglers would continue to have their sport after the natural supply of fish began to run low. Tanks of little trout and other fish were hauled in by truck or wagon and released to grow up in the wilds. But there are some wilds which can't be reached by road. And anyway, a copter is faster. The Washington State game department already swears by the whirlybird as a trout planter, and others are eager to try it out as soon as more copters are available.

Wildlife experts have also used the copter for census-taking. Every year it's necessary to calculate the size of animal herds—elk and deer particularly. If a herd has increased greatly, men have to bring the animals extra food for the winter. Or part of the herd may actually be rounded up and taken away in trucks to a spot that offers good natural grazing. If something has happened and the game population has diminished, hunting will be restricted. Again, because a copter can fly low and slow, it's perfect for searching out the shy animals and estimating their numbers.

Trappers, too, need to know the size of the fur-bearing animal population. You can tell approximately how many muskrats there are by counting their homes or hutches. Since they live in swampy country, the easiest way of surveying and counting is to pay them a visit by helicopter. While the game warden is at it, he can also watch for hunters and trappers who are operating illegally out of season or without a license.

And for the rest of us, who seldom see wild animals except in the movies, the copters do a job, too. A movie company has already made a film of African animals, using the cabin of a helicopter as a traveling crane for the camera. Because a whirlybird is such an all-around useful machine, it has become the naturalist's newest tool—and one of his best.

After scouting for leads through arctic ice floes, the copter returns to the ship.

Crew of icebreaker in Bering Sea gets set for action as Coast Guard copter ends scouting.

Canada's icebreaker, d'Iberville, has flight deck built in, not added to the ship.

Wilderness work of another kind is done by helicopters operating from special ships called icebreakers. These powerful, sturdy vessels plow their way through ice in harbors, rivers and bays, breaking it up so that ordinary ships can follow. Or, if a vessel is icebound, the icebreaker can come to the rescue and set it free.

The new Canadian icebreaker, the *d'Iberville*, is the first to have a special helicopter hangar, repair shop and flight deck built right into the ship. (Other icebreakers, including our country's, have copter facilities built on their regular decks.)

The pilot's job aboard the *d'Iberville* can be any one of a dozen things. He can take off and scout ahead, radioing back information about the ice—where it seems to be heaviest, where the easiest path for the ship would be. In August, when the ship starts her long journey to the Arctic, a doctor and a dentist go along. Word may come that patients need care inland from the ports where they call. Off the medical men go by helicopter. Some Arctic waters have never been charted, and land has not been mapped. For these jobs, and for low-level aerial photographing, the copter offers the best of help.

Much of Alaska has now been surveyed and mapped by men in copters hired by the United States government from commercial owners. Working along with military and other government craft, they have covered the endless wintry wastelands that could not be surveyed for decades by any other means.

The wilderness areas of the world are real frontiers, just as real as any the pioneers faced in years gone by. And the helicopter fits right into frontier life.

The copter comes back to the deck of the d'Iberville after flying a dentist ashore.

4

TREASURE DOWN BELOW

"THAR SHE BLOWS!"

That's been the cry from the lookout in the crow's-nest of whaling ships for two hundred years or more. The crow's-nest is a little platform high on the mast. There a sailor stands and peers all around at the sea, watching for the spout that a whale blows into the air when it comes up to breathe.

Now it's different on some whaling ships. The lookout is a helicopter pilot, and he flies his crow's-nest to the whale, instead of waiting for the whale to happen along.

In the cold waters near the continent of Antarctica, Alan Green, an English helicopter pilot, has spent three whaling seasons with the Norwegian ship *Thoroshavet*. Green's heliport is the fantail, or rear deck of the ship. On an average working day, he puts in about four hours' flying time. From his moving perch he can survey a hundred times more ocean than a man ever could from a stationary post on the mast. The *Thoroshavet* has rolled up record catches for the industry, too.

Green in his helicopter can do even better than the old-time lookout. He can spot a whale *under* water, before it comes up to blow. Then he reports its location by radio. Fast killer boats set out from the ship. Guided by the radio, they head for the place where the whirlybird is riding herd on the whale. Harpooners on the killer boats go into action, while Green speeds home. For safety, his copter has flotation gear so that he could land on the water in emergencies. But so far he's always set her down aboard ship.

If a man in a helicopter can spot a whale, why shouldn't he drop down to a few feet above the ocean and actually make the kill? Someone has invented

The look-out for today's whaling ship is a pilot; the crow's-nest is his chopper.

a device for doing just that. Using a special sort of gun, the pilot can fire from hovering position. The bullet explodes inside the whale, then lets off a gas which keeps the dead animal afloat until the ship can steam up alongside and get it.

SCOUTING FOR TUNA AND SHARK

Other seafaring folk have put helicopters to use, too. Off San Diego, California, tuna fishermen rely on a Hiller copter to locate schools of the big, fierce fish. In the past the fishermen's search was hit or miss, and a lot depended on luck. The boat, with a lookout in the crow's-nest, had to cruise slowly around, hoping to run across the tuna's path. Nowadays, if there are any tuna to be found, the copter pilot finds them and leads the fishing vessel by radio right to the spot.

Several years ago, fishermen along the California coast got word that some-

If tuna are around, the pilot will spot them and radio directions back to the boat.

thing unusual was happening. Soup-fin sharks had been sighted here and there near shore. These sea creatures have enormous livers which sell for a fabulous price to makers of vitamin preparations. But the soup-fins don't show themselves very often, so the news of their appearance caused a lot of excitement. The hunt was on. One fishing outfit hired a copter to patrol the water north of Los Angeles about half a mile out. Sure enough, the pilot could spot the sharks. What's more, he even shot one with an explosive harpoon head. Then all he had to do was throw down a marker to show the fishing boat where the prize could be picked up.

WINGS FOR PROSPECTORS

Locating riches that lie under the surface of the ocean is a natural for the whirlybirds. So is the search for treasure under the earth. In many parts of the world, helicopter prospectors fly around looking for new oil fields and new veins of metal-bearing ore. Sometimes the copter simply takes the place of a pack horse. It transports men and equipment far beyond the spot where the last road ends. But at other times it actually carries instruments for prospecting from the air.

One such instrument is the magnetometer—a device for measuring gravity, the force which pulls things toward the earth. Perhaps you may think that gravity is the same everywhere, and that if you stub your toe, you fall down just as hard in Maine as you do in Colorado. For ordinary purposes that is true. But there really are differences in the pull of gravity at different places. You couldn't notice the variations because they are very, very tiny, but the magnetometer is so delicate that it can pick them up and make a record of them. The important thing is that an expert can read the ups and downs on the record and can tell from them where certain minerals lie deep down beneath the surface of the earth.

Of course, it would take years to walk up and down over a mountain area, doing detective work with a magnetometer. But a helicopter can do the job in days, flying back and forth with the instrument sticking out like a turtle's head through the plastic bubble in front.

DOODLE-BUGGERS IN THE AIR

Another new gadget, called a scintillometer, looks like a big pistol which the prospector "shoots" at the ground. It has been used in exploring for new oil fields, and it may turn out to be the best thing yet.

The scintillometer is a sort of extra-sensitive geiger counter which picks up radiations coming from the edges of oil pools hidden way down below. The prospector wears earphones so he can hear the messages sent out from underground. Of course, he has been trained to decode the signals. If particularly interesting ones come through, he asks the pilot to put him down. The helicopter settles gently just where he wants to land, and he hops out to do further detective work. Sometimes he can't be sure that the signals are the real thing. Perhaps stray cosmic rays or other radiations have set his machine to buzzing in his ears. He can often make sure by taking samples of earth to the laboratory for further testing.

Copter pilots call this kind of job "doodle-bugging." That's because in the old days people called doodle-buggers used to hunt for water wells in a similar, if unscientific, way. The doodle-bugger (he was also called a dowser) walked around with a forked stick in his hand. The stick was supposed to attract water the way a magnet attracts iron. When the dowser thought he felt something pulling the stick downward, he marked the spot, and there the well was dug. If he had struck water, of course, he said the magic dowsing stick was responsible. If he made only a dry hole, he kept mighty quiet about it and dowsed some place else!

It's a long way from dowsing to flying around with a scintillometer, but this newfangled doodle-bug really works. A big area can be tested in almost the time it takes to tell about the operation. And the copter saves the scientist the effort of trudging on foot or plodding along on a horse.

Thanks to the whirlybird, off-shore oil workers are able to get home each night.

THE NEWEST WILL-O'-THE-WISP

Most oil companies still hunt for their buried treasure in the old, pre-atomic way. But some of them have found that whirlybirds can speed up prospecting, especially in marshy country.

Sometimes an oil-hunting copter carries a pilot, a prospector and an instrument called a gravity meter. Like the magnetometer, this device measures differences in the earth's gravity, and the trained operator can tell from his record whether or not the rocks in an area are likely to surround pools of oil.

The meter itself has to rest on a little three-legged table called a tripod. For convenience, the tripod is rigged so that it slides down through the floor of the cockpit. The pilot lands the copter on its pontoons in a marshy spot. Next, he cuts his engine and waits for the rotor blades to stop, because the least vibration will upset the delicate machine. Down go the tripod legs into the earth. The prospector sets the meter in place, switches on electric current from a battery under the seat, and takes his reading. In a few minutes, the whirlybird is up and away to the next place on the oil-hunter's map.

An older method of hunting oil uses little man-made earthquakes. This is how it is done: First the prospectors make a survey and carefully mark the places where they will drill holes and set off blasts of TNT. On dry ground, men have no great problem. They can walk around and set up their surveying

Today, slow-moving marsh buggies have given way to helicopters in oil exploration.

and drilling instruments easily. But for work in swampy country, oil companies have used huge trucks called marsh buggies, which are really half boat. The buggies carry men, equipment and an instrument called the seismograph. When the TNT blasts are set off, the seismograph picks up the vibrations in the earth. By looking at the record of these vibrations, scientists can tell whether there is likely to be oil down below.

Now suppose you add a helicopter—or two or three—to the party that goes out in a marsh buggy. The job really begins to move. Instead of plowing slowly back and forth through the swamp in the buggy, a man in a copter swoops along above the ground. The machine settles gently on its pontoons at the right place and makes a steady platform for the surveyor's instruments. Another whirlybird actually drags chains and electric cable from spot to spot over ground too soggy for men on foot. It also carries TNT safely in wooden tubs slung from the fuselage. The buggy, with the seismograph aboard, can wait quietly in one spot.

Finally, helicopters have brought peace to a long-standing feud in the swamps. Long before marsh buggies were invented, trappers had discovered wealth in the muskrats that make their homes under the soggy earth. But the great wheels of the buggies crushed the animals' burrows, killed the young and ruined the trapping. Now the marsh buggy just makes a few tracks in and out. All the scouting and jockeying is done by helicopters above the earth. The muskrats stay safe in their runs—until the trapper comes along.

64

DOING FERRY DUTY

Some of the most valuable oil reservoirs lie beneath the bottom of the sea, miles from shore. Drilling and pumping in these places is called an "offshore operation." To the offshore oil worker, a helicopter is a sight as welcome as the dove was to Noah in his Ark. Until recently, the men had to work on barges anchored out at sea. There they lived for ten days at a time, then went home by boat for four days' leave. At best, the water was choppy, and they got seasick going back and forth. A storm might mean accidents and long delays in reaching the doctor.

With whirlybird taxis, not only the men, but the boss, can feel more cheery. First of all, the men work a normal eight-hour day, five-day week, ferried back and forth by copter from their homes on shore. They have been freed from life on the barge. Their flying ambulance is ready for any emergency, too. And nobody gets seasick on the way to work.

IN URANIUM COUNTRY

Newest on the list of prospectors for buried treasure are the uranium hunters. Helicopters have helped them, too. Let's have a look at operations in Monument Valley in southern Utah. This wild desert area is about as far

The helicopter takes surveyors to rich Canadian ores where no rails or roads lead.

from a railroad as it is possible to get in the United States. Automobile roads are almost as scarce as rails. Until recently, no surveyors had even gone through to make maps of the country. But one day prospectors found out that thin bands of yellow in the sandstone formations carried valuable uranium ore. The rush was on, and of course, people needed maps. Helicopter pilot Sammy Chevalier and others were called in to help government surveyors make the maps as fast as possible.

It was Sammy's job to taxi a surveyor and his instruments from their camp to the tops of bluffs or mountains—or anywhere else the map makers had to go. No matter where he set his copter down, Sammy was at least a mile above sea level. That caused special problems. The air grows thinner the higher you go, which means less air for the copter's rotor blades to chew into. Still, Sammy managed to get the surveyors where they wanted to be—that is, until hot weather came. It got really hot by June in Monument Valley. When the thermometer stood at 110, the heat thinned the air so much that it wasn't sensible to go on with routine operations.

Even before summer came, Sammy had been making most of his flights in the early morning or late evening when the air was cool. On trips to very high country, he chose his landing spots carefully. Whenever he could, he settled down right at the edge of a cliff. Then, for the take-off, he would literally make the copter fall off the edge of the mountain, instead of forcing it to rise higher into the thin air.

This trick of Sammy's is only one of hundreds that pioneer pilots have invented, as their helicopters add a new dimension to the hunt for treasure beneath the surface of the earth or the ocean.

5

GROWING THINGS

SO FAR AS WE KNOW, A HELI-
copter hasn't yet been used for plowing a field. But whirlybirds have done
almost everything else on a farmer's list of chores.

Just to keep the record straight, nobody claims that a copter is an all-around
complete miracle machine for farmers. They still need tractors, cultivators,
reapers and a barn full of other instruments. Each crop still has to be handled
in pretty much the old and tested ways. But there are individual jobs on
almost any farm which whirlybirds do faster—or easier—or better.

Take rice planting. In many places it is done entirely by hand. But at least
one rice grower has successfully planted his seed from a helicopter, flying
slowly back and forth across the flooded field. The rice is soaked in water
first, until it's almost ready to sprout. By that time the seeds have absorbed
a lot of moisture. They are heavy and they plop down just where they're
supposed to go.

Some of the ranchers in the California foothills have also hired a copter
to plant barley and other grain. The pilot takes off with the seed in bins or
hoppers on each side of the fuselage. Fifty or a hundred feet above the field,
he opens the hoppers and the grain flows out through fishtail dispensers in
the rear. At the far end of the field the pilot climbs, makes a swift hammerhead
turn, and in two or three seconds has started back on the next row.

Copter sowing is particularly good in hilly country where the slopes make
hard, slow work for tractors. In flat fields most farmers still find they can plant
grain more economically with ordinary machines which drop the seeds in
rows only a few inches apart. But then comes the problem of getting the weeds

Whirlybird's downwash drives spray close to earth to kill the dreaded black fly.

out. It doesn't pay to grow the grain plants far enough apart so that a hoe or a cultivating machine can chop weeds. And imagine going over a huge field by hand! In recent years, scientists have discovered special chemical sprays that kill weeds but leave the grain plants unharmed. Of course, the best way is to spray down from the air, because tractor-drawn spraying equipment squashes a lot of the plants as it rolls along. An airplane can fly above a field, and in many places that's the way the job is done. But a helicopter does it better.

Even the slowest plane must swoop across a field fairly fast. It misses corners and the far ends of many fields, because the pilot doesn't dare come too close to fences, bushes, trees and telephone wires. A whirlybird pilot can take his time. He can nuzzle slowly up into a corner—or even back in, if it's a tight spot. Barley fields that have been weeded by helicopter several times between February and July produce up to one-fourth more grain than they used to!

Tomato and bean fields give the farmer a different kind of headache. It's easy enough for him to weed them with a tractor and cultivating instruments. But there the plants stand, all by themselves, ready for hungry insects to eat. Of course, the chemists have invented insect-killing sprays and dusts which can be squirted over the plants in many different ways. Tractor-drawn instruments and crop-duster planes do a wonderful job for farmers every year. Still, helicopters can do it better. They are safer than airplanes, too. Although the pilots of duster planes are highly skilled, it's dangerous to swoop down close

68

Fogging by helicopter yearly saves the forests from killing blights or disease.

enough to spray a low-growing crop thoroughly. An equally skilled copter pilot can creep along safely very close to the ground.

What's more, the downwash of the rotor blades adds a finishing touch to the dusting and spraying. It actually creates a doughnut-shaped current of air that goes down to the ground, then circles back upward. This means that the chemicals, blown by the downwash, reach not only the tops of leaves, but also the undersides where many chewing insects attack.

Copters can dust at night, too, when the air is heavy and still, with no wind to blow the chemicals away. Men holding carbide lanterns stand around the edges of the field. That's all the pilot needs to guide him back and forth in the dark.

WHAT TO DO ABOUT WEATHER

To some farmers, insects seem less of a menace than frost. There's no

In a fight against beetles a Hiller 360 sets out on a spray mission in Switzerland.

Flying low and fairly slow, the copter pilot puts the spray where it's needed.

A mosquito breeding place is a danger no more when a copter has sprayed the area.

chemical yet invented that will keep the weather from suddenly turning cold! One freezing night can nip the blossoms in an orchard and ruin a whole crop. For years fruit growers have tried to solve the problem by lighting small fires in smudge pots. That's a disagreeable chore, and the pots give off a nasty black smoke to which the neighbors often object.

Now—you guessed it—a helicopter comes to the rescue. It blows a warm breeze over the trees. The principle of the thing is easy to see if you think of the times you've stood around in a chilly room saying: "My shoulders are warm enough, but my feet are freezing." That's because warm air rises and cool air falls. So, by using that wonderful downwash, the helicopter pilot circulates the air around the sensitive fruit trees. The rotors force the warm upper air downward, stir up the cold layer below, mix it all together and circulate it again. Unless the cold snap is a really bitter one, the downwash breeze is enough to save the crop. It's been known to raise the ground temperature by as much as ten degrees.

Warm weather comes, cherries ripen. It's just about time to pick them, and then clouds cover the sky. A drizzle falls, but the clouds stay. Every twig on the trees is dripping wet, and with no sun to dry them, the cherry stems begin to absorb moisture. Before long the fruit will swell and the delicate red skins

71

The versatile eggbeater dusts a citrus grove . . . and sometimes saves it from frost.

will burst, unless something can be done quickly. The call goes out for that old dependable downwash again.

Back and forth over the orchard goes the helicopter, blowing raindrops away. Later in the season, the pilot dries out a field of ripening tomatoes in the same way and saves the crop. Farmers have found, too, that the helicopter fan is enough to break a thin water film on the skin of fruit so that it dries quickly without getting moldy or sun spotted.

ODDS AND ENDS

Walnut and pecan growers have found that it's a lot easier to shake nuts off the trees with a well-aimed downwash than to harvest the crop by hand.

And in cotton country harvest time brings a small flock of whirlybirds in. The cotton can be picked more easily if the leaves have been removed from the plants. This is called defoliation, and it's done with a killing spray, which copters spread with precision up and down the rows.

This ability to get the spray exactly where it is needed, and nowhere else, is another great advantage the copter has over the duster planes. Farmers often want to use on one field a chemical that would damage other plants growing in the next field. The helicopter pilot can travel low enough to keep the

72

Downdraft from the rotor blades of this Army chopper saved a $250,000 cherry crop.

Note how the downwash of this copter forces the chemicals under branches and leaves.

chemicals close to the ground and slow enough to aim them just where they ought to go.

The list of miscellaneous helicopter chores around the farm stretches on and on. Celery is harvested from wet fields where trucks often get bogged down in the mud. But a copter can land gently on its pontoons or skids, pick up the heavy lugs of celery and hop out again at top speed. In Arabia, date growers have used the helicopters to pollinate their date palm trees. And the same rice farmer who sowed his fields from a copter also uses it to scare away birds that want to eat the tender young shoots.

Anybody who wants an odd job done by helicopter these days has to hire the machine by the hour or by the day. But many a farmer and rancher dreams of the time when he will have his own whirlybird in the barn—for fun as well as chore work. He can't afford to do it now. A copter would cost him as much as ten reaping machines. Of course, if he has a huge farm or ranch, it is a different story. In fact, one of the world's biggest ranches does have its own helicopter. The half-million acre Waggoner spread in north Texas bought one in 1952 and put it right to work on the range.

EGGBEATING COWBOYS

For a number of reasons, the vast Waggoner outfit decided that a copter was a sensible investment, not just a big-scale stunt. First of all, the old-fashioned kind of cowboy is hard to find these days. Punching cattle sounds romantic, but it takes a man way off into lonely country, far from his family. He puts in long hours at difficult work. There are plenty of better jobs for the average hard-working, sociable human being. The Waggoner Ranch wasn't actually going to pot because it lacked cowhands, but the big boss was looking toward the future.

So, one day at roundup time, an odd combination of men went to work out on the range. The regular cowpokes rode their horses as usual. The chuck wagon brought along the cook with his supplies. But the top cowhand sat in the plastic bubble of the helicopter, swinging his rotors instead of a lariat. Up he went from the dusty plain and buzzed off toward a thick jungle of mesquite —a tough, fast-growing shrub that has been making life more and more miserable for ranchers. As mesquite spreads over the ranges, it offers shelter to bunches of wary animals that don't care to be rounded up. The thickets are impossible to see through from horseback, hard to ride through—and painfully time-wasting. A rider can scout around in the mesquite for hours looking for just one ornery cow and her calf.

Not so the airborne cowboy. Hovering above a patch of jungly growth, he spots the critters hiding there. Chances are that the very presence of the copter and its unusual overhead noise will scare the whole bunch of cattle into a run

74

One copter cowboy does the work of 20 horsemen during roundup time on the ranch.

Airborne cowboys on the Waggoner Ranch spot strays, broken fences . . . and coyotes.

for open country. There the men on horses can begin hazing them along toward the general roundup. Any stubborn beast that sticks to shelter will be spotted from the air. The copter pilot simply marks its exact location on a map. Then he flies off toward the nearest rider, hovers and hands the map out, not even bothering to land.

In between roundups, the copter does regular cowboy duty, too. A man can spot broken fences as well from the air as from the back of a horse—and a whole lot faster. He can inspect the condition of cattle all over the range. If the animals are bothered by insect pests, the copter pilot flies out and dusts them with bug killer. Next, he may fly a repairman with tools and parts to fix a broken windmill that pumps water for range cattle. Or he may fetch the doctor to mend the broken leg of an unlucky bronco buster. Altogether, the Waggoner Ranch boss figures that his one copter does the work of fifteen to twenty skilled cowboys.

A rancher still can't use a helicopter to dab his brand on a calf, but he can take it out to hunt coyotes and wolves which kill the calves. He doesn't even have to climb out of the cockpit to shoot. In the air the whirlybird can chase a varmint, and make every dodging motion that the four-footed creature makes. Sitting comfortably a few feet above the killer, a man can take good aim and be sure that one more danger to the range has disappeared. On top of everything else, he can enjoy riding in a copter as much as he enjoys riding a fine horse.

THE FARMER'S BEST FRIEND

All these farm and ranch jobs are important and exciting. But for something really spectacular you have to go to Argentina, where for years locusts had been eating up the crops on a grand scale. The Argentine locusts themselves belong in a class with DC-3's. Each one of them is nearly three inches long. They hatch out by the billion. When they get well under way they form a black cloud that actually darkens the earth for an hour or more. With a roar like a fleet of airplanes, they fly in a swarm five miles wide, twenty miles long and twenty feet thick. You can imagine what happens to a field of corn when the locusts decide to eat. The ground as far as you can see is soon covered with nothing but crawling insects, inches deep. And when they can find nothing better, they descend on range grass, leaving not a mouthful for cattle to eat.

By 1947, half of Argentina's crops were endangered by the locusts. All the usual methods of killing the insects had been tried. Airplane spraying helped, but it wasn't sufficient. For one thing, a plane couldn't fly right into the locust swarms because the creatures got into the carburetor and cylinder fins and gummed them up. A plane could spray poison down onto the ground, but that only killed off the locusts at the top of the thick, crawling carpet. The rest could get away to eat, lay eggs and start another horde.

Then came helicopters. The Argentine government ordered, not one or two, but ten, to make war on the pests. Working in teams of two, the copters plunged right into the midst of the flying swarms because their engines weren't vulnerable and didn't get clogged up with the insects. Then the pilots climbed and sprayed down from the top. Finally, they polished off any stragglers that still crawled on the ground. In many places they were able to kill 98% of the swarms.

When it was all over, a lot of young Argentinians began learning how to fly and service their farmers' best friend.

6

BUILDERS FOR THE FUTURE

IT WAS A WONDERFUL SITE for a dam, all right. But how was anybody going to build it? Even beavers couldn't do the job. Men would have to work for months at this remote spot in the Canadian woods, just blasting out a road up the steep, rocky face of an eleven-hundred-foot cliff. An elevator as high as the Empire State Building could do the trick, of course, but you don't find elevators of that size in the wilderness. So a helicopter took over the job.

High on the cliff, engineers spotted a ledge that could be enlarged by blasting. Up went men with drills and dynamite, and before long they had a niche in the rock fifteen feet square, just large enough for the helicopter to perch on. Above that, at the height of the rotor blades, they blasted back into the cliff far enough to give clearance to the long, whirling wings.

Meanwhile, trucks were bringing in sand, cement and equipment which they dumped at the end of the road several miles away. Now shuttle service could begin between the road and the top of the distant cliff.

One morning the pilot set his copter down on the road. Men heaved bags of cement and sand onto two special platforms built out from each side of the fuselage. A load of 400 pounds, evenly divided between the platforms, was about what the pilot knew he could carry. Taking off almost straight up, he sailed over the tops of the tall trees and plunged upward toward the place where his tiny heliport had been gouged out of the solid mountain rock. Six minutes later he set his machine down there as accurately as a steady hand fitting a key into a keyhole. In a few quick jerks the men had the bags off the platforms, and the helicopter was swooping back toward the road.

A thousand trips later, material for the dam had all been hoisted into place. The whirlybird had done in a few weeks a job that would have taken many months to do if the engineers had waited to construct a road. For the first time in history, a flying machine had been the pack-mule that made it possible to build a dam.

In between pack trips, the pilot did emergency service with his helicopter when men needed to see the doctor in the nearest town. And sometimes he taxied dam builders to the movies, besides. His copter proved to be a new tool in construction, a kind of free-wheeling elevator. What's more, people just naturally felt better about working in the wilderness, knowing they weren't stranded a hundred miles from anywhere.

Engineers in California thought they had a similar place for a dam, but they weren't sure. So they hired a copter from the Rotor-Aids Company in Ventura. Men with core-drilling equipment traveled by whirlybird up to the rocky area among the peaks. Sure enough, their tests showed they had found a good dam site.

Rotor-Aids' machines also pioneered in another part of those same California mountains. Piece by piece, they ferried a whole oil-drilling rig, plus

In British Columbia a mountain-crawling tractor was supplied with fuel by a Bell.

79

nearly ten thousand feet of pipe, up to an inaccessible hilltop. They did the job in three days. Later, the copters hauled the equipment out—after the drillers had struck oil.

PIONEERING

Not one helicopter, but nine, have been at work on the biggest construction job of all. Up in British Columbia, the Aluminum Company of Canada picked out a spot for a new smelter and power plant. Dams would be built to provide water for the electric power station. Then towers would be set up for high-tension wires to carry electricity to the smelter. And all of this had to be done in a wild mountain forest area that hadn't even been fully mapped when the project started.

No roads led into the wilderness. But the engineers wanted to set up their construction camp on a mountain top, without waiting for roads. So they put an unusual team of machines to work. A transport plane carried a great crawler tractor to a valley as close to the mountain as possible. Then the tractor started out under its own power, creeping and bulldozing its way uphill through snow. That kind of work takes plenty of fuel, and a helicopter provided it. Flying a Bell 47, the pilot carried loads of diesel fuel in five-gallon cans from the valley

When the tractor reached the top, the copters began bringing in building supplies.

to the tractor on the mountainside. It took five days for the big crawler to make the climb, with the copter buzzing back and forth like an anxious mother bird.

As soon as the tractor had leveled off a space on the mountain, copters began to bring in building materials and men, and, most important, things the men needed: food, stoves, blankets, tents. Then came lumber and engine parts and machinery. Some of it arrived in Bell 47's. Some came in big Sikorsky S-55's. Like an eagle bringing food to its nest, the S-55 hauled loads in a sling under the fuselage and set it down gently on the snow in a circle of waiting men.

Sometimes, to speed up delivery, loose materials were loaded into boxes, carried to the camp and shoved off the copter while the pilot hovered close to the ground, ready to speed off again without landing. At first sawdust served as a packing to cushion things inside the boxes against the fall. Later on, popcorn proved to be much more satisfactory! And in a year of operation, not a single box broke.

Thanks largely to the copters, the engineers can count in months, not years, the time that the whole vast project will take.

Men, machinery, fuel, lumber . . . everything was brought to the camp site by copter.

In other parts of the world, power companies have used helicopters to string high-tension wires across country. On mountainous Oahu in the Hawaiian Islands, for example, power lines had to cross rough, wild country. Flying low over newly-built pylons the whirlybird unreeled five miles of wire in five hours as easily as a fisherman can let out his line. In England a copter did a similar job, skimming along among beautiful ancient trees that men would have been forced to cut down if ordinary stringing methods had been used.

Sometimes a copter's work on power lines begins long before the wires are ever strung. It takes up photographers and engineers, flying as slowly as they need to go, letting them study the best and shortest power-line routes.

Then, after the construction men have finished their work, the copter still stays on the job. High-tension wires have to be watched constantly. Until recently, inspection was done by men on foot or on horseback. Slogging along afoot, an inspector can take care of about forty miles of line in a week. But suppose you take him up in a helicopter. He can work twenty times as fast— and do a better job. Flying along forty or fifty feet from the wires he can watch over 800 miles of power line a week.

Did you ever try walking all day with your head back, looking at something against the sky? Even when you're used to the job, you get mighty tired. What's more, you can't be sure of seeing things accurately. But when a man looks down at towers and power lines against the darker background of the earth, he can see much more sharply, and it is much less tiring.

Some of the things inspectors look for are broken or frayed strands of wire, rust, cracked or burned insulators, tree limbs that have grown too close to the line—and birds' nests. From his comfortable seat in the copter, a man can often spot trouble that an inspector on foot might pass by for weeks or months. If he notices anything suspicious, he can ask the pilot to stop and hover for a while so he can take a good long look. Occasionally he may even carry along special instruments for measuring power leaks.

The vast power system of the Tennessee Valley Authority uses copters to inspect its lines. So do companies in the West and Northwest. Although a whirlybird isn't cheap to operate, it has saved so much time and headache that it actually makes money for the operators. It frees skilled linesmen for other, more important work. Now they can help in building new lines or repairing old ones, instead of spending a great deal of time walking over rough country.

Besides this routine kind of job, a copter pilot sometimes gets called out for special duty along the lines. Freezing rainstorms mean big trouble for high-tension wires. Heavy ice crusts weigh them down and finally break them.

Patroling power lines by whirlybird, a man can check 800 miles of wire a week.

A copter can't melt the ice off, but it can shake it off. Using the downwash from the rotor blades, the pilot worries the lines until the ice breaks free and falls harmlessly to the ground.

Power companies and people who operate dams for irrigation and water supply have to find out in advance how much water they can count on when the spring thaws begin. They can make a pretty good estimate by measuring the depth of the snow in various places. And the easiest way for measuring-men to get there is by copter.

When winter comes in Oregon, for example, Dean Johnson straps a pair of skis and a pair of snowshoes to his helicopter, which is already equipped with skids of its own. Then he goes out—not for sport, but for the serious business of learning how much snow has fallen in the mountains. At place after place he lands the copter, puts on either the snowshoes or skis (depend-

Laying cable by copter saved time, money, and an English forest from the axe.

ing on the kind of snow he finds) and sets out. With his measuring rod he estimates the amount of snow in this area. Then he flies off to the next place.

TROUBLE SHOOTERS

Construction men, engineers of all sorts, have turned to helicopters to solve their problems. Once the Army had to put up a control tower for an emergency airport. A hoisting crane was needed to lift the top part of the tower into position. But the crane was broken. Then somebody had a bright

With skis, snowshoes and a copter, Dean Johnson measures snowfall in the mountains.

idea: call a copter. Sure enough, the copter pilot lifted the structure, hovered to make sure he had it over the right spot, then set it neatly in place high above the ground.

Another time, the builders of a huge factory chimney forgot to provide any way of cleaning the 159-foot structure. They simply left off any ladder or climbing cable. Then along came a trouble-shooter in a helicopter. He hovered near the chimney top and in no time had dropped hooks over its edge. Block and tackle attached to the hooks supported a cleaner's platform, which could then be pulled up from the ground.

At least one steeplejack has actually leaned out of a hovering copter, attached his rigging to a chimney, and then climbed out onto it. This saved him the tedious job of hoisting himself up with ropes and safety equipment.

Perhaps the most unusual trouble-shooting of all was done in planning a telephone company microwave tower near Boston. Engineers had to find out quickly just how high the tower needed to be. They could have worked it out by old-fashioned surveying and a lot of mathematics. But they didn't. Instead they placed a mirror on top of the telephone building in Boston and sent up a copter over the hill where the tower was to be built. Then, when the sun was in the right place, they caught its rays in the mirror and reflected the sunbeam

Despite high, thin air, a Bristol 171 makes a good landing at Gurnigl, Switzerland.

off toward the distant hill. The pilot moved slowly up and down watching for the flash of the distant mirror. When he caught it just right, he looked at the altimeter and verified the copter's altitude. Then he could tell the engineers how high the tower had to be to catch the microwaves when they flashed out as the sunbeam did.

On the frontier in the wilderness—and on the latest microwave frontier of modern science—a helicopter is a pioneer in every sense of the word.

7

RESCUE FLIGHTS AND
MERCY MISSIONS

AT THE TIME OF THE BIG
storm, in 1945, Jimmy Viner was Chief Test Pilot for the Sikorsky helicopter
factory in Connecticut. Jimmy went to work that cold November morning
thinking that the gale had almost blown itself out. It had been bad enough
ashore, but he knew it must have been worse for men on ships at sea. All
day before, and all night, waves had been pouring up onto the Connecticut
beaches. Down at Pennfield Reef—a ledge of jagged rocks—spray was explod-
ing high into the air. If any vessel approached those hidden knives of stone,
it would surely be cut to pieces.

Hours before Jimmy entered the factory trouble had indeed started for two
men at sea. Somewhere out on the water the storm had lashed into a tugboat
that was towing a barge loaded with oil. Waves of earthquake violence tore
the barge loose and set it racing toward shore. The barge had no power of its
own. The two men on board could not steer it. And so the clumsy vessel
plunged closer and closer to Pennfield Reef. Then it struck the rocks and hung
there like a helpless worm on a fish hook.

Watchers on shore got to a phone at once, calling the police. But the police
were helpless, too. No rescue vessel could hope to get through the pounding
surf; but if it did it would surely be crushed on the reef before the men could
be taken from the barge.

Then someone had a crazy idea. A few miles away was a factory where inventors and pilots were trying out a new kind of flying machine. They had

talked a lot about what their oversized eggbeaters could do in the air. Maybe this was a chance to find out how good a helicopter really was.

The call to the factory went through. A few minutes later, Jimmy Viner was sitting at the controls of a Sikorsky H-5. Beside him was Jack Beighle who knew how to run the rescue winch the helicopter carried.

It would be murder for an airplane to buck this weather and the surging, pounding wind. But a helicopter was different. A stiff wind would actually make it easier for the pilot to keep his machine hovering over the barge! Jimmy Viner started his engine. The rotors chewed into the wind, and he headed off toward Pennfield Reef.

Before long he was over the stricken barge. Jimmy stopped the H-5 in mid-air and Jack Beighle began to reel out a line on the winch. A heavy weight on the line kept it from flipping around, and the powerful downwash from the rotor blades helped to aim it right onto the deck of the barge. Hovering there in the gale that blew spray past them, Jimmy and Jack waited.

An astonished man appeared in the doorway of the barge's cabin. Then, hanging onto the door jamb with one hand, he stretched out the other and caught the dangling rope. He attached something to it and presently waved, signaling for Jack to reel in the line.

While Jimmy's hands and feet kept busy holding the helicopter steady, Jack untied a water-soaked note from the end of the line.

"Barge got leaks in about eight tanks," Jack read, shouting the words. "The cabin is full of water and we have no heat. The barge is in danger of breaking up. (Signed) Captain."

There was no time to waste, Jimmy figured. He had to get those men off right away. So he held the whirlybird where she was while Jack manned the winch again.

Down went a rescue belt attached to the line. A man scrambled out onto the flooded deck and fastened himself in the belt. Soon the winch had reeled him up. Jack helped him into the helicopter's cabin. There he huddled, shivering and wet—but safe.

There was room for only three in the H-5—Jimmy, Jack and the rescued crewman. Down below stood the barge captain. And every passing minute might be the last one for the battered craft. If you had the decision to make, you'd probably do what Jimmy did—even at the risk of scaring the daylights out of the unhappy captain.

The rescue belt went down again. Then, when the captain was secure in it, Jimmy shifted his controls. The copter swooped toward shore and final safety —with the captain dangling at the end of the rope over the snarling water.

The bargemen were alive and whole, after sixteen terrible, helpless hours on the reef. Jimmy had snatched them away just in time. A little while later, the broken pieces of their craft were being pounded to bits on the rock.

Jimmy Viner's rescue mission—the first of its kind—was performed only a very few years ago, in 1945. But since then, helicopters have kept on doing equally wonderful and amazing things.

For instance, there was a beautiful lazy day when a man and his wife went down to a beach in Hawaii. It was too warm and comfortable even for swimming. So they just lolled back in their blown-up inner tubes and floated. Too late, they realized what was happening. A treacherous current had pulled them off shore and was sweeping them out into the open sea.

Luckily, the pilot of a helicopter got to them in time. He buzzed up and dropped a rubber raft for the two frightened people to use. Then, with the downwash from his copter's rotor, the pilot fanned the raft safely to shore against the tide!

Clear around on the other side of the world, in the Belgian Congo, a pilot did exactly the same trick. Flying along above the Congo River one day, he sighted a raft with a terrified passenger aboard. Apparently the man had been working on a construction project farther up the river, when the raft broke loose and began to float downsteam. Either the man couldn't swim—or he was afraid to try. And just a little way ahead, the river plunged downward in fatally rocky rapids.

Using the copter's rotor to stir up a wind, the pilot blew the raft from midstream to the safety of the river bank.

Then away he went, never knowing whose life he had so casually saved.

Earthquake victims in Greece run to the helicopter that brings them food supplies.

To demonstrate rescue methods, helicopter crewman hoists swimmer aboard by cable.

CONGO COPTERS

Mercy missions of quite a different sort make up the daily work of this pilot and others in the Belgian Congo. Their regular job is insect fighting. Already they have wiped out so many mosquitoes that the mosquito-carried disease, malaria, is a rare thing. Before the copters came, almost everybody there had malaria.

The Congo is also the home of something infinitely worse—a small insect called the black fly, which lays its eggs underneath the skin of its victim. The eggs hatch and the tiny wormlike larvae go to work. They cause such an itching that people are almost driven crazy. You don't die from an itch, of course. But wounds, infected from scratching, can and do kill people.

The black fly is a vicious creature, and she has a habit that in the past made her almost impossible to deal with. She stays close to the ground. You'll never find her more than forty inches up in the air. If you want to kill her with a poisonous spray, you can't do it just by flying over the treetops with ordinary airplane spraying equipment.

Helicopters in the Belgian Congo have brought relief to at least part of its

90

inhabitants who live in and around the city of Léopoldville. Spraying—called "fogging"—kills malarial mosquitoes as well as the black fly. The copters' downwash drives the spray close to earth where it's most needed, and the whirlybirds can descend into jungle clearings to give an extra helpful dose to people's houses.

So far, the copters have made a good beginning. Some day they may lick the black fly in the whole huge Congo area. Meantime, the pilots have an unusual life. Occasionally they come face to face with hippopotamuses only a few feet below. Elephants have got so used to the copters that they don't even look up when a fogging machine buzzes overhead.

STORM!

These Congo copters belong to Sabena, a Belgian airline company that operates a fleet of whirlybirds in Europe, carrying passengers and mail. Sabena pilots have also done their share of rescue work closer to home. In February, 1953, a violent storm hit the coasts of Belgium and the Netherlands. Before long, eighty-mile winds had driven huge waves through the dykes, and many Dutch villages were flooded. About three o'clock one afternoon, Sabena got a desperate call from the mayor of a town called Middelharnis. A dozen people were huddled on a little strip of dyke nearby. Nothing but a helicopter could save them.

Although the wind seemed too wicked even for a copter, the pilot, Gérard Tremerie, thought he could make it. Off he went. When night came, his friends gave up hope. The rumor spread that Tremerie's copter had crashed. But it hadn't. Next day, the wind-battered pilot was able to report his activities. In addition to rescuing people from isolated dykes, he had flown injured to hospitals, had brought food to flooded villages, and had carried engineers around surveying ways to stop further storm damage.

COAST GUARD COPTERS

The Belgian pilot's heroic work was part of an already impressive story about flood rescue. In 1949, our own Midwestern states were hit by rains that made rivers overflow their banks. Nobody knows how many people owe their lives to the speed with which the Coast Guard helicopters picked them up from the housetops or barns where they were marooned. Perhaps it seems strange that the Coast Guard should operate so far away from the ocean, but there are many jobs the Guardsmen do on rivers and in the Great Lakes region.

Credit for the first mercy mission ever performed by a helicopter in this country goes to the Coast Guard, too. In 1944, the U.S. destroyer *Turner* exploded at sea near Sandy Hook on the New Jersey shore. Soon the beach was dotted with injured men who needed blood plasma—more of it than the

Winch-operated cable in this Royal Navy copter hauls an Admiral up from a ship.

Minutes after this pilot bailed out, "Last Chance Taxi" pulled him from the sea.

nearby hospitals had. In answer to an SOS, a Coast Guard pilot took off in a snowstorm from New York with a load of plasma—and he got it there in time.

Commander Frank Erickson, an early Coast Guard helicopter enthusiast, was responsible for developing some of the equipment that has made rescues so successful. He worked out the idea for the hydraulic hoist which lifts people into a hovering whirlybird. He invented one of the types of rescue belts that is tied to the end of the hoist line.

Almost since the beginning, the Coast Guard has considered it routine to fly citizens of the stormy, isolated Cape Hatteras region to the hospital on the mainland. For the first time in its history, this rugged area on the North Carolina coast has been able to count on adequate medical care.

Day in and day out, the bright yellow Coast Guard machines do every kind of chore—from picking a couple of scared boys off an old half-destroyed bridge in Massachusetts, to hauling five fishermen out of battering waves when their boat sank near the California coast.

IN TIME OF NEED

Another time, at another spot in California, a fisherman climbed out on a point of rocks at low tide. He got so absorbed in his sport that before he knew

When floods swept over Holland, helicopters went on daily searches for survivors.

93

With Civil Defense workers, a whirlybird demonstrates rescue of a trapped victim.

it, the tide had come in and cut him off from the beach. There he stood in his high rubber boots with swirling water rising all around him. Between him and the shore, breakers pounded over the rough rocks. He would be dashed to death if he tried to wade back.

Fortunately, helicopter pilot Ted Leopold was making routine flights as he dusted a farmer's field near the beach. As he rose to make a turn at the end of a run down the field, his eye caught the frantic fisherman out in the boiling surf. Leopold had no rescue gear with him. He was rigged for crop dusting. But like most pilots, he carried a rope. After tying one end of it to the copter, he threw the other end out and headed for the fisherman.

The stranded man grabbed eagerly at the rope, and Leopold hoisted him quickly across to the beach. A minute later the pilot was again making his slow, low flights back and forth over the field, leaving behind a cloud of chemicals that meant more life to the growing things there.

94

Trapped by a rising tide, a fisherman is hauled to safety by a Coast Guard chopper.

It was a quick switch from lifesaving to life-giving, and one was just as easy as the other for the pilot. His trip to rescue the fisherman had done something that no other lifesaving device could have done in time. The wonderful fact about a helicopter is that the rescuer can perform his normal, safe work, while at the same time he snatches others from death. The great thing about Leopold was that he had the right tool to use—and that he thought quickly enough to use it at the right time.

8

PASSENGERS AND MAIL

IS IT FUN TO RIDE IN A COP-
ter? It certainly is. Suppose you are one of the passengers who travel in the
whirlybirds that belong to the Port of New York Authority. (They are mostly
visiting dignitaries or officials of the Port Authority.) And suppose that pilot
Sammy Chevalier is going to take you up.

You'll start out from the top of a tall building in New York City. First by
elevator and then by a flight of steps, you reach a platform built on steel stilts
above the building's roof. This is the heliport, forty feet square, with a big
yellow bull's-eye in the center. The bull's-eye is what Sammy aims for every
time he comes down. He hits it, too. But just to make people feel better, a
scoop-like net of heavy wire surrounds the landing spot, which looks very small
to ordinary folks.

You get into the cab and fasten the safety belt. Sammy starts the engine and
the rotors whirl. In a few minutes you begin to get a strange and wonderful
feeling that the air is a rubbery substance, bouncing you a little, then lifting
you up.

"Maybe you better not look down at first," Sammy tells you, if he thinks
you're a little tense. But you probably can't help yourself. Down you look,
through the plastic bubble that surrounds the cockpit—down toward the
crowded, crawling traffic below. It seems as if you're about to plunge over the
clifflike side of the building. For a second you want to grab onto something.
And then you know that you're perfectly safe. You can relax and just have fun.

Some people say that a helicopter makes you feel as if you were being swept
along through the air in a basket at the end of a rope. Others say it's a little

Heliport in Brussels is hub of Sabena Belgian Airlines' passenger copter service.

Heliport No. 1 is an official landing area for New York City's Police helicopters.

New York Airways' "Skybus" passes a hospital on its New York-New Jersey mail route.

like a Ferris wheel ride. Anyway, it's something that more and more passengers will be discovering for themselves. They won't be occasional special passengers, such as the ones Sammy Chevalier taxis around. His copter belongs in the class called "executive" aircraft, which means it is operated for officers of the company, or guests.

SKY TAXIS

The real passenger copters are bigger than the executive machines, and they go on regularly scheduled flights. The first air-bus service in this country was started in 1953 by New York Airways. Its copters carry four passengers, plus pilot, and some mail or air freight, making short hops between the three big airports around New York City.

Military transport copters, of course, had already been ferrying up to twenty passengers at a time, and they had proved that the idea was perfectly practical. The first big helicopter airliner went into service in England, also in 1953. It is a huge, two-engine craft that can carry eighteen passengers on trips as long as two hundred miles.

With this experience to go on, people in other cities have been dreaming of air-taxis and air-buses. You still can't commute to work every day by whirlybird, but that time probably isn't far off.

Circle atop Lincoln Tunnel, connecting New York-New Jersey, marks landing spot.

The fact is, helicopters promise to be our safest means of rapid travel. Of course, there are airplanes that go faster than helicopters. But that doesn't mean that a plane is always the fastest way of getting you between two points. Airports are usually located far from the centers of big cities. You often spend as much time struggling through ground traffic to the airport as you spend flashing through the air in a fast transport plane. So, for trips up to a couple of hundred miles between cities, a somewhat poky helicopter gets you from place to place sooner than a jet plane could.

The time is probably coming when you'll go across the continent by a combination of jet plane and helicopter. The copter will pick you up in the center of Los Angeles, say, and taxi you to the airport where a jet transport is waiting. With a roar and a whine, the jet will rise from the immensely long field and hurtle you toward another airport on Long Island. There you'll transfer to a taxi copter, which will set you down on a rooftop in the heart of New York.

Sammy Chevalier makes a bull's-eye landing on Port Authority Building in New York.

WHIRLYBIRD MAIL

One reason why passenger service can be worked out easily is that much pioneer work has been done by pilots who fly the mail. Men in the Post Office Department began to dream about using helicopters almost as soon as they heard that there was such a thing. Air mail already traveled fast by plane across the continent, but it often ran into bottlenecks close to home. With a copter, air mail could be speeded from downtown centers of big cities straight to airports, and then on its way by plane. Copters could also pick up and deliver mail and parcel post between big cities and suburban towns.

In 1946 the Post Office dream began to come true. Soon there was heli-mail service in and out of Chicago, Los Angeles, and New York. In some places, copter service has cut the delivery time of air mail in half. Clarence Belinn, who operates the Los Angeles Airways mail copters, was worried at first about the project. What would people say when they discovered whirlybirds flying over their homes every day? He took precautions—at least he tried to. He planned to have mufflers on the copters so they would make as little noise as possible. But somebody at the factory forgot to put the mufflers on. The mail had to be delivered with noise. And to Belinn's great surprise and relief, nobody squawked! In fact, his whirlybirds turned out to be spellbinders. People loved them from the first, because for one thing they were less dangerous than airplanes—but mostly because they were just whirlybirds.

THE MAILMAN AND THE MINKS

The Post Office in Canada discovered even more enthusiasm for copters when it began experimental service in Newfoundland. Around Gander Bay, snowbound fishing towns sometimes had to wait two months in wintertime before mail could be delivered by dog sled. By copter, they began getting it about every ten days!

Canadian pilot Bob Cooke found that he could rely on willing helpers, too. Every time he needed to refuel at one of his regular gasoline dumps, there was a copter enthusiast waiting to pump it for him. On one trip he learned that a woman in the little town was desperately in need of hospital care. Cooke landed close to her door, then flew off with her, quite certain that any minute she would be dead. Nevertheless he set her down at the hospital in time for the blood transfusions that saved her life.

About the only Canadians who didn't consider the whirlybird a blessing were the minks on a mink ranch. For some reason the copter terrified them. They went into such a stage of decline that their owner protested to the Post Office. His business was being ruined!

YOU CAN'T BEAT AN EGGBEATER

Los Angeles mail pilots were the first civilians to use night flying instruments in their copters. They were also the first mailmen to help prevent traffic jams. This is the story:

Every New Year's Day brings to neighboring Pasadena the world's record traffic. People stream into the city for the Rose Bowl football game and the giant parade, or through the city to the horse races at Santa Anita. Altogether more than a million human beings in 400,000 cars are on the move in Pasadena on that day—they are, that is, until traffic jams hold them up.

Things were really bad until someone had the bright idea of taking the Chief of Police up in a helicopter. So the mail pilot and his machine were borrowed from Los Angeles for the day.

Riding along in the slow-moving copter, Chief Clarence Morris could spot the intersections where cars were beginning to pile up. Then, by radio, he passed word along to traffic cops on the ground. Before long oncoming cars were re-routed to less crowded streets.

In the past Morris had flown over New Year's Day traffic in a light plane, but he confessed he didn't feel too well about it. The pilot had to fly as

Traffic officer in a Bell helicopter keeps close watch to prevent a traffic snarl.

Helicopter pilot radios officer on the ground condition of traffic in the area.

slowly as possible so that the Chief could see what was going on. But slow flying in a plane isn't the safest thing in the world. If the pilot had to make an emergency landing, he would find every space that was big enough already packed with cars. A copter, on the other hand, could at least find a spot on a roof or in somebody's back yard.

To take the cork out of traffic bottlenecks, says the Chief, you can't beat an eggbeater!

9

"LAST CHANCE TAXIS" OR THE HELICOPTER AT WAR

"THIS IS REDCAP ONE. MY wingman is down. Let's have a copter and some cover. Now!"

It was the firm but almost frantic voice of a fighter pilot that came crackling over the radio at Air Rescue Service headquarters in Korea. It was a call for help that would send a helicopter on another rescue mission behind the enemy lines. Within a few minutes the tiny unarmed and unarmored whirlybird would come skimming through gunfire and smoke at tree-top level to snatch back to safety another fighter pilot who had been forced to crash land in enemy-held territory. It was another mission that had earned the helicopter the favorite nickname, "Last Chance Taxi."

Today, thousands of brave young men are alive, happy, and at home with their families because the helicopter was there when the weary soldiers and airmen needed it most. Many of them, picked up right off the battlefield, traveled by copter direct to hospitals. If necessary, the pilot could even give blood transfusions to patients in the air.

In Korea, often called "the proving ground of the copter," the whirlybirds did many things. They delivered men, medical supplies, food, ammunition, and guns to troops fighting to hold their positions on a battle line. They scouted enemy territory and helped soldiers to aim rocket launchers and Howitzer cannons. Many times the helicopters were called upon to lay communication wire, and they did in minutes a job that used to take hours of hard and dangerous work by soldiers of the Signal Corps.

Leathernecks climb aboard a chopper for an aerial invasion of Hill 812 in Korea.

Combat-ready Leathernecks hit a Korean hilltop from a giant HRS-1 Sikorsky copter.

Oftentimes, all that was needed to silence enemy guns was an Army copter hovering overhead. The enemy knew that if he fired his guns when the "hoverbug" was there he would give away his position and the copter pilot would call in the Air Force or Marine fighter planes to blast him out of his stronghold.

Even traffic snarls on Korean mountain roads were unraveled by the Military Police who hovered overhead and radioed directions to the truck drivers below.

On one occasion, Army engineers flew a bridge into position, piece by piece, so that the United Nations' forces could move up into new territory. Another time, ten H-19 Sikorsky helicopters flew 34,000 pounds of food and ammunition to infantrymen whose supplies were running low.

The anti-aircraft guns of an enemy are a big problem to high-flying troop carrier planes, but those guns are only a minor problem to the ground-hugging copter which skims along at tree-top level, ducks behind hills, and takes cover in canyons. In Korea, Army helicopters flew nearly two thousand missions, and only one helicopter was lost to enemy fire.

PACKHORSE FOR THE MARINES

The men of the Marine Corps put the copter to work in Korea in still another way. The Marines learned from experience that when they forced the

Marine Corps' new XHR2S takes on one of three jeeps through its clamlike doors.

Sikorsky H-19 shows its muscles by easily lifting a "Mighty Mite" towing truck.

enemy to retreat and moved in to occupy his bunkers or dugouts, they had to rebuild those bunkers before they could use them for their own fortifications. The Marines' guns had damaged them so badly that they had to be rebuilt before they could be used. Then, while the Leathernecks were busy repairing the damage and making the bunkers useful again, the enemy would sneak back and counterattack, and oftentimes recapture their positions.

But the Marines and the copter solved that problem. Rear-area troops sawed bunker timbers to just the right lengths. Then the timber, along with gunnysacks to be filled and used as sandbags, were loaded into the copters.

In Korea badly needed ammunition was delivered to front-line troops by whirlybirds.

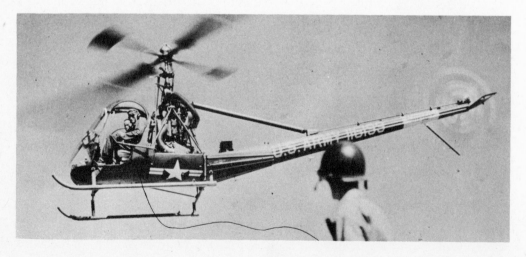

When the Army has to lay telephone wire in a hurry, the Hiller H-23 does the job.

At the cry, "Attack," infantrymen jump from H-19's and run for combat positions.

Getting wounded men to base hospitals quickly saved many lives in Korea.

109

The jet-powered XH-26 was designed to be dropped from a plane for evacuation duty.

The whirlybirds hedge-hopped along behind the advancing troops. Once the enemy fled a bunker, the copter would set down and unload the timber and sacks. The advancing Marines would hustle the logs into place and fill the gunnysacks to close up open spots. Quickly and easily the bunkers would be rebuilt and made strong enough to withstand heavy fire by an enemy bent on recapturing lost ground. No spot on any craggy peak in Korea—or any place in the world, if need be—is too inaccessible for the copter.

BUSY CHOPPERS

The Navy, too, has added the helicopter to its forces. When a Navy fighter plane takes off from the deck of an aircraft carrier, there is always a copter hovering nearby. Should a plane falter and fall into the sea on take-off, the copter is there for the rescue. Or when the Navy boys head back to their flat-tops after a mission has been completed, the fleet's "choppers" hang on their rotors, waiting to go to the rescue of any pilot whose plane can't quite make it back to the fleet. Plucking a gasping airman from the briny sea is practically a daily duty for the versatile copter.

Sunday is a busy day for the copters, too. Every Sabbath the Navy's whirly-birds fly chaplains to the ships of the fleet so that church services are held for all. The chaplain of the fleet, no matter where the fleet is at sea, is flown by copter from one ship to another to conduct Sunday services.

The Korean War was the first time the helicopter was used under actual combat conditions, and it proved one fact to the officers and men of the Army, Marines, Navy and Air Force—the helicopter has brought about many changes in military ideas. Major General G. H. Higgins, commanding general of the famed 82nd Airborne Division, foresees large helicopters capable of transporting tanks and large numbers of troops, complete with supplies and equipment, as mainstays of the Army. The day will come when heli-troops will replace paratroops. Today, when paratroopers bail out of high-flying transports, they are often severely injured. With helicopters able to transport safely, and de-

The Navy's Piasecki HUP is called "Retriever," which is just what it is doing here.

Whirlybirds at sea rest on the deck of the USS Sicily as it cruises Korean waters.

Flotation gear fits around wheels of Piasecki YH-21 and can be inflated when needed.

When operations call for visits to other ships, the Admiral makes it by whirlybird.

Navy copter delivers chaplain to each ship of the fleet for Sunday church services.

liver anywhere large numbers of troops, there will be no more need for the dangerous bailing-out from aircraft a mile up.

The Navy, too, has under construction "choppers" that could be used for searching out and sinking enemy submarines. Equipped with electronic devices that can detect the whereabouts of a submarine in the waters below, this copter could hover and drop depth charges to sink an enemy "fish."

SMALL AND MIGHTY

Still one of the most important of all jobs the copter performs for the military forces is that of rescuing. In peace, as in war, the helicopter has become the "Last Chance Taxi," the small but mighty machine of the mercy mission.

For instance, there was the cold February day when Lieutenant Edward Brej got word that a B-36 had crashed in the snowy wilderness of Labrador. Fifteen men were anxiously waiting for a copter to save their lives. When Lieutenant Brej reached the scene, however, he quickly realized that this would be no routine rescue. To get to the men, he had to bring his copter down into a circle of trees for a landing in deep, powdery snow.

You may find it hard to believe that a pilot could say anything but good about his rotor's downwash. He can use this man-made wind to dust crops, to harvest nuts, to warm a fruit orchard and to save lives. But there in Labrador,

Patterned effects of downwash are shown here with an H-19 hovering over Han River.

A litter on each side, USMC whirlybird carries injured men back to base hospital.

Lieutenant Brej knew his rotor's downwash would create a problem instead of solving one.

As he neared the ground, a thick, blinding, white blanket suddenly surrounded him. The downwash had attacked the powdery snow and sent it swirling upward. Unable to see a thing, Lieutenant Brej had to grope his way down in a blizzard of his own making.

But in a few hours all fifteen men had been carried to safety from a desolate spot that could only have been reached overland after several days of travel. And those days meant the difference between getting the men out alive—or not getting them out at all.

Lieutenant Brej belongs to the Air Rescue Service of the United States Air Force, and saving people's lives is his business. He and other pilots in all branches of military service have flown so many mercy missions that officials have stopped counting the number of individuals saved.

Air Rescue Service men stationed in Alaska have learned to expect almost anything in their day-to-day work. Once they carried an injured trapper from his isolated cabin to a hospital. Another time they picked up a hunter who had been trampled by a moose that went berserk. And then there was the man who was always forgetting to put enough gasoline in his little private plane. Three times in three weeks the Air Rescue Service was called on to fill up his plane's gas tank, somewhere far back in the Alaskan wilderness.

Marine Sergeant shows position he used to snipe Communist line crossers in Korea.

Wounded soldiers on the French Indo-China battlefront are rescued by an HTE-2.

A Coast Guard copter picks up a sailor. Note flotation gear on copter's wheels.

In the old days before the helicopter, airplanes would fly as close as possible to the scene of an emergency call in Alaska. Then men with sleds and dog teams went the rest of the way to inaccessible spots. Now, of course, the whirlybird takes rescuers and medical supplies anywhere that dog sleds could take them, and they do it in minutes instead of days.

Even on training flights, the pilot of an Army copter can find special work to do. In Oklahoma, for instance, Fort Sill is close to the Wichita Mountains Wildlife Refuge, where about a thousand buffalo live under government protection. Every year the new calves have to be vaccinated against disease. This means that the whole herd, except for the meanest old bulls, must be rounded up. It's a hard job for the buffalo cowboys, because their horses are afraid of the big, shaggy beasts. Then the Army boys came to the rescue. Pilots learning to fly military copters began to make training flights over the Refuge, and there's nothing they like better than shooing stray buffalo down out of the hills.

Again the copter proved itself the small but doughty machine for any kind of mission.

If terrain is so hazardous a copter can't land, para-medics jump to aid the injured.

Wounded soldier is strapped in special copter stretcher for flight to rear area.

10

CALL A COPTER!

IN ADDITION TO ALL THAT you've read, here are some simple and useful—or strange and wonderful—jobs that copters have done:

Once, when important test flights had to be made at an airfield, a flock of buzzards appeared. The big, slow-flying birds might have endangered the test pilots. And so, hunters in slow-flying copters brought the buzzards down.

Another time, model airplane builders had scheduled a contest. And then came rain—just enough to muddy the field and make it unfit for use. A copter pilot flew over the ground again and again, using his downwash to dry up the mud so that the contest could go on.

One year, tourists nearly ruined the hotel business in a part of the Adirondack Mountains by staying away. They'd heard about a sudden plague of little biting flies that made life miserable in the mountains. A helicopter fogged the area with DDT spray and cleaned out the flies in time to save the trade.

Santa Claus lands on the rooftops of some department stores in New Jersey and Pennsylvania nowadays. By helicopter, of course.

As a publicity stunt, a copter was once hired to fly a golf caddy—not the player—around a golf course.

Several newspapers have helicopters for gathering on-the-spot news. The pilot-reporter for the Oregon *Journal* once saved four lives when he went out to get the story of a disastrous flood.

Coast Guard helicopters have proved to be the best way of getting supplies to lighthouses on dangerous rocky islands.

Flying just behind horses, a chopper-borne cameraman takes movies of the race.

Racing Steward in a copter keeps a look-out for possible fouls by trailing race.

An archeologist, flying in a copter over the jungle in Central America, located ancient Indian ruins never before seen.

Hanging onto a line tied to a copter, skiers in the mountains have been towed up hard hills by a soft-hearted pilot.

Some wild dogs in New Jersey turned vicious and began attacking people. Men in a copter chased the dogs and shot them.

Big ships often need to have their sides inspected for rust or other possible damage. Men can pull themselves up and down on board platforms, but it's a tedious job. Inspectors in helicopters do it quickly, and with pleasure.

Once, some sailors wanted to go swimming, but they were afraid of sharks. Up went a copter, and the pilot acted as lookout while his friends swam in peace.

English policemen, wondering if a copter would be useful in trailing criminals, rigged up a test. Some of them pretended they were trying to escape in a car. Others took out after them in a copter. The mock criminals really did their best and put their heart into the game. The cops in the copter finally got them. And the "crooks" said the worst part of all was the feeling that they couldn't possibly get away, no matter how they turned and dodged along back roads.

Recently, the pilot for a construction company in Canada noticed an automobile on fire on a lonely back road. He set his whirlybird down alongside, grabbed his fire extinguisher, and had the blaze out in no time.

At least once a lumber company has used a copter instead of a truck. Trees were felled in a part of the forest where it would cost a fortune to build a logging road. The helicopter landed in a clearing, took the logs aboard, and flew them to the sawmill.

The next time you go to the movies, you may see something like this: The opening scene shows you an aerial view of a town. It begins to come closer. Your eyes are focused on one particular house—then, closer and closer, on one window of that house. You can be pretty sure this film was photographed from a helicopter.

And so, no matter what the job is, more and more people have begun to say, "Call a copter!"

Voting is for everyone, so ballot boxes in Canada are coptered to remote areas.

11

HOW THEY FLY

LIKE ALL BIRDS, WHIRLYBIRDS have wings. The rotor blades lift a helicopter and make it fly. At first glance a rotor doesn't look much like an airplane wing, which we know is fixed to the fuselage. But if you examine the blades you'll see the resemblance. (Figure 1) Blades really are wings, and that's why we call helicopters rotary-wing aircraft. Before we figure out just how the blades work, we'd better take a quick look at some facts about air itself.

You probably know that air is a mixture of invisible gases. That means it is made of countless tiny particles which float all around us constantly, although we can't see them. We can brush these particles aside so easily that we don't

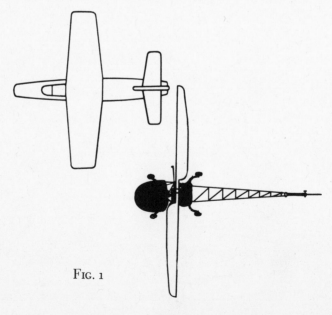

FIG. 1

122

even feel them as we walk along. A handful of air seems to weigh nothing at all. Nevertheless, air does have weight. Scientists have measured it. They have found that, at sea level, air presses against us with a weight of about fourteen pounds for every square inch. This figures out at more than a ton of pressure on the book you're holding as you read now! You can see that the pressure of air is something tremendous to work with.

Why isn't the book squashed right out of your hands? Because the air presses against it *equally* from every side. The half-ton downward pressure is balanced by an equal upward push of half a ton.

The wing of an aircraft is much bigger than a book, so the total pressure of air against the wing is many, many thousands of pounds. Of course, the upward and downward pressures balance each other when the aircraft is on the ground. But suppose you could increase the pressure against the bottom of the wing or decrease the pressure on top. Wouldn't the wing rise up? It certainly would, if the changes in pressure were great enough. (Figure 2)

That is the whole secret of what makes heavier-than-air machines fly.

Air Flow

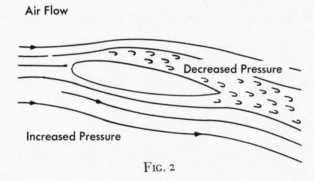

FIG. 2

SKIING ON AIR

But how can we upset the balance of the two pressures? First of all, we must have motion.

You may have experimented with the changes that motion can make. Although it's not a wise thing to do, you have probably stuck your hand out through the window of a car. When the car first creeps along, you feel nothing unusual. But when it begins to travel fast, your hand is forced backward. (Figure 3) Motion has upset the balance of air pressures. Why is this?

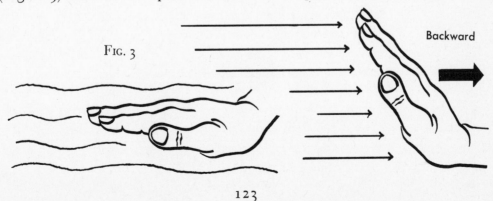

FIG. 3

Backward

When the palm of your hand moves very slowly through the air, it bumps into the little invisible particles of gas. But they flow out, around and back so quickly that you don't feel any change in pressure. Then the car carries your hand along much faster. Air particles begin to pile up against your palm in a sort of traffic jam. They press much harder than the air at the back of your hand. You feel this change in pressure that has been caused by motion. Your hand is pushed backward.

Now suppose you tilt your palm a little toward the front of the car. Something else happens. All of a sudden you feel your hand rising—exactly as if it were skiing uphill! By tilting your palm, you have redirected the push of the traffic jam. Instead of forcing your hand backward, the crowded air particles force it upward. (Figure 4)

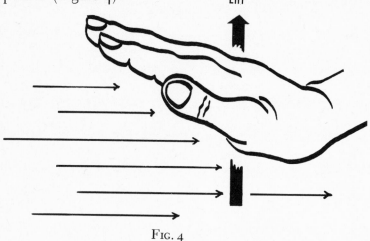

FIG. 4

The same thing happens when you launch a kite in the air. You pull it forward, tilted at an angle. The pressure on the underside of the kite increases, because air particles begin to pile up faster than they can spill away around the edges. Since the kite is tilted, it rises, as if it, too, were skiing up a hill of air.

Motion through the air has upset the balance of pressures on the kite. Pressure on the underside was made greater, and so the kite flew. Does the same thing happen to an aircraft wing?

Yes, it does. When a moving wing is tilted slightly, you get the same skiing effect. The wing rises into the air.

UP SHE GOES!

This is just another way of saying something that the Englishman, George Cayley, said more than a hundred years ago. You will remember that he was one of the first to build helicopter models, and also one of the first scientists to figure out why his model flew. He said that flight came from "the application of power to the resistance of the air."

When you fly a kite, you provide power—and motion, of course—by pulling it along. The traffic jam of air particles is the same thing as Cayley's "resistance of the air."

Now, when a kite goes up, it takes its tail along. It has enough "lift" to carry the extra weight. One of the big problems that early aircraft inventors had to solve was the problem of making wings lift more than their own weight. Part of the answer was increased power: more power meant more lift. But that was not the whole answer. Scientists discovered that the shape of the wing was very important. A wing with a rounded nose and a gently backward curving top surface could lift nearly three times as much as a plain flat wing. Figure 5 shows what a cross section of this kind of wing looks like.

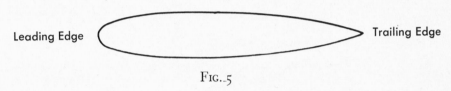

Leading Edge   Trailing Edge

Fig. 5

Why does a curved, or cambered, wing work so well? The reasons are very complicated. The practical fact is that it does work. A properly shaped wing has so much lift that it can carry the whole aircraft and its load up into the air.

These are only a few of the facts about flight. You can find out more about it in the books listed on page 157. Meantime let's put the wing we've been talking about onto a helicopter. To make the story simple, we'll take a copter with a two-bladed rotor (Figure 6). And, for the moment, we'll just concentrate on the blades, going back later for a look at all the other parts of a whirlybird. The small rotor, like a propeller in the tail of our copter, has nothing to do with lifting us off the ground.

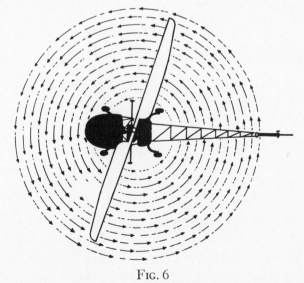

Fig. 6

The blades of the main rotor are, of course, connected with the engine which turns them round and round. They are also built so the pilot can change their tilt as they move through the air. This tilt is called the *pitch* of the blade.

You'd better stop and look at the picture to be sure you know what pitch means, because it is going to be important from now on. (Figure 7) The picture shows a cross section of a blade. The solid outline shows the blade with its underside parallel to the ground. The dotted outline shows it tilted upward. That means its *pitch* has been increased. Remember that tilting, or increasing the pitch of a blade, takes advantage of the skiing effect during flight. It increases the pressure on the underside of the blade and helps to give it lift.

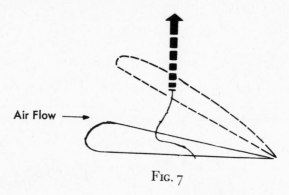

Air Flow →

FIG. 7

Now imagine that we want to go straight up. The pilot starts the engine with a self-starter much like the one on an automobile. The blades begin to turn. Since the blades are wings, motion is going to make them lift us. The pilot feeds the engine more gas. The blades whirl faster. If you looked down at the copter from above, you could not see the individual blades. They are whirling too swiftly for your eyes to follow them. Instead, you would think you were looking at a greyish disc. Helicopter engineers use the word disc when they talk about the circular path of the blades through the air. (Figure 8)

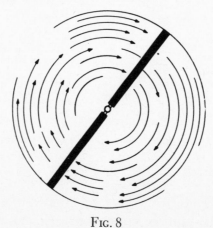

FIG. 8

The pilot feeds the engine still more gas to give it more power. At the same time he increases the pitch of the blades. Luckily, inventors have given him a wonderful stick which takes care of both these jobs in one motion. They have combined the throttle (which controls the amount of gas that is fed to the engine) with a lever which changes the pitch of the blades. It's called the *collective pitch* stick, because it gives the same pitch to both blades at the same time.

To go up, the pilot pulls up on the stick with his left hand. Automatically he gets the right combination of power and pitch to keep the blades whirling at the right speed. With more power and more pitch—the copter leaves the ground. The blades lift evenly, and the copter rises straight up into the air. (Figure 9)

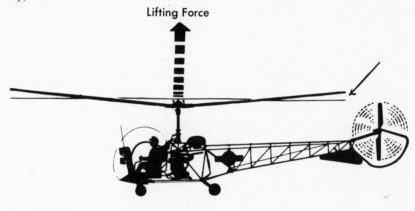

Lifting Force

Fig. 9

HOVERING

Here we go—but how far can we go? The record helicopter climb in 1953 was 22,289 feet above the earth. At great altitudes the air becomes very thin. The thinner the air, the more pitch the blades must have in order to get lift. Average copters can rise about 11,000 feet. (The pilot will say his machine has a "service ceiling" of 11,000 feet.)

But suppose the pilot wants to stop and hover somewhere below his service ceiling. What does he do? He moves the collective pitch control to adjust the pressures of air on the blades. The whirling wings must have just enough lift to keep gravity from pulling the copter down to earth, but not so much lift that the machine keeps on rising. The right combination of power and pitch will make the blades hold the copter in hovering position. Of course, the pilot must learn by experience to feel out this combination—just the way an automobile driver learns how much to turn the wheel and make the car go where he wants it to go.

AND DOWN AGAIN

Now suppose the pilot wants to come down. He can let gravity do the job of pulling him down. But at the same time he must be in control of the machine. He pushes *down* on the collective pitch stick. This decreases the power to the blades and their pitch to maintain the right speed. The whirling wings lose part of their lift. And so the copter comes slowly down.

A CUSHION OF AIR

Some of the early, unsuccessful helicopters were able to rise a few feet off the ground, but no farther. Here is the reason for this odd quirk:

As the rotor whirls it churns the air into a downward-blowing wind. This is the useful downwash you have read so much about in earlier chapters. About two million cubic feet of air a minute are displaced by the blades. That's a lot of air to be going some place in a hurry. First it whooshes downward. The earth stops it and makes it bounce upward. But it can't bounce straight up. It has to go to one side or the other, because the rotor is forcing more air down all the time. The result is a sort of doughnut-shaped circulating current. (Figure 10)

The air inside this doughnut is thicker and heavier than normal air because the rotor keeps forcing more and more of it down faster than it can bounce back up or escape to the sides. A moment or two after the pilot first starts his engine there is a regular cushion of this slightly compressed air all around the copter. Now the heavier air exerts more pressure on the undersides of the blades. What happens? The copter rises more easily than it would in normal air. That is, the blades don't require as much power in heavy air as in normal air.

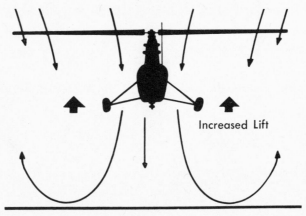

Increased Lift

FIG. 10

Up goes the copter. But when it is a few feet above the earth it stops rising—unless the pilot gives it more power and pitch. The downwash now has farther to travel before it bounces. The doughnut-shaped cushion has grown fatter, so the air in it has more room. That means it isn't so thick and heavy. If the pilot doesn't give the rotor more power and pitch, the copter will drop down a little, then rise, then drop—again and again—as if it were bouncing on a cushion of air!

You can see what happened to the early copters. Their engines and rotors were good enough to produce lift—as long as the heavier air of the ground cushion helped out. But they weren't good enough when they got beyond the cushion and had to work in more normal air.

THAT PINWHEEL ON THE TAIL

While our copter's engine is turning the blades it also turns the small propeller in the tail end of the fuselage. On an airplane, the propeller is the thing that gives forward motion. But not on a helicopter. Before we see how a whirlybird flies forward—or backward or sideward—we'd better take care of the propeller, which is usually called a tail rotor. Another name for it is "anti-torque rotor." Torque means "twist." The tail rotor keeps the fuselage from twisting round and round during flight.

Torque itself is something that scientists call a *reaction*, and they have discovered a rule about it. "For every action," they say, "there is an equal and opposite reaction." You know about this rule if you've ever fired a shotgun. The action happens when the bullet shoots out of the muzzle. The reaction is the backward kick that the gun gives to your shoulder.

Another kind of action is that of a whirling electric tool—a hand drill, or a polishing machine. Start the motor on one of these and you can feel the reaction. While the motor whirls the drill-bit or the polishing pad in one direction, the motor itself seems to behave like a live thing in your hand, trying to turn in the opposite direction. Of course, it isn't "trying." What you feel is simply the reaction, which is called torque reaction. (Figure 11)

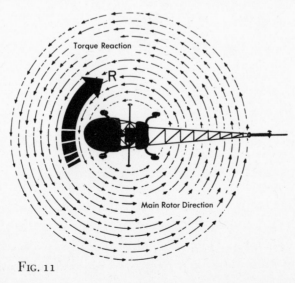

FIG. 11

The whirling action of a helicopter's blades is caused by the engine. Can we expect a torque reaction from the engine? We certainly can. Since the engine is fastened tight to the fuselage, the whole body of the helicopter will turn in one direction, while the blades turn in the opposite direction. It will, that is, unless something stops it. That's the job of the tail rotor—the anti-torque rotor.

The little blades of the tail rotor bite into the air, the way an airplane's propeller does. If the torque reaction is turning the fuselage to the left, the tail rotor pushes to the right and holds the copter steady, with its nose pointed straight ahead.

Actually, this little piece of machinery does more than you might think. The pilot controls it with the foot pedals and uses it as a rudder. (Figure 12) If he wants to swing in one direction, he makes the tail blades bite more strongly into the air. To swing in the other direction, he reduces the bite to almost nothing and lets torque do the work. Then, when he's turned far enough, he gives the blades only enough bite to hold the copter steady.

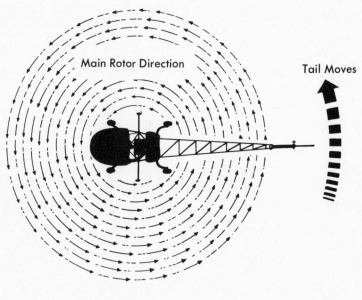

Main Rotor Direction

Tail Moves

FIG. 12

FORWARD AND BACK

Now let's take the copter somewhere besides up and down, round and round. Suppose the pilot wants to go forward while at the same time he goes up.

You can get a picture of what happens if you think once more about the way the whirling blades look. They seem to form a disc like the disc of a helicopter toy. Pretend for a moment that the disc is real and that you have fastened it tight to a stick in your hand. If you want to aim it straight up in the air, you hold the disc parallel with the ground. But if you want to aim it up and forward, you tip the disc forward a little.

Now you have a mental picture of the disc slanted forward *as a whole*. But what are the individual blades doing?

The tip of each blade is rising as it goes toward the tail and dipping downward as it comes toward the nose. We've already seen that increased pitch makes a blade rise, and decreased pitch makes it dive downward. So the pitch of each blade must now change as it whirls. While blade number one gets more pitch on its way toward the tail, number two gets less pitch on its way toward the nose. Then number two gets more as number one gets less. (Figure 13)

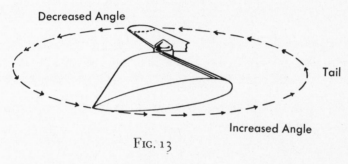

FIG. 13

Surely, you may think, no pilot could do this rapid-fire shifting of pitch. Not without help, of course. The pilot uses a lever called a *cyclic pitch control*, or *cyclic stick*. He simply moves the stick with his right hand, and the stick in turn regulates the blades so that they change pitch at the right moment.

Remember that the main rotor lifts the copter upward while at the same time it tips forward to aim the machine ahead. At last the pilot wants to stop climbing and go straight forward. He simply tips the rotor a little more. (Figure 14) The blades still do enough of a lifting job to keep the copter aloft. But, instead of rising any more, the copter slips along forward at a faster speed.

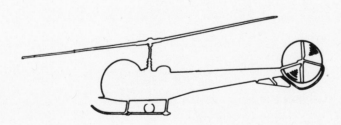

FIG. 14

Flying backward or sideward is equally easy. The pilot moves the cyclic stick and tips the rotor in the direction in which he wants to go—backward left or right. Everything else works just as it does in forward flight. (Figures 15, 16, and 17)

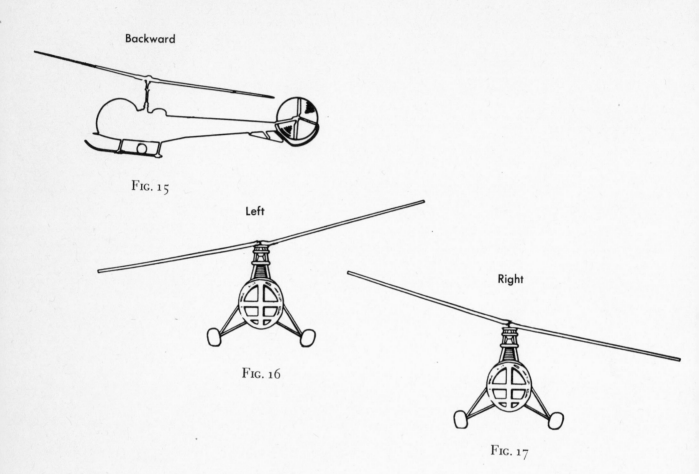

Backward

FIG. 15

Left

FIG. 16

Right

FIG. 17

TURN AROUND

Our helicopter has done everything now except turn around and come home. To make a turn the pilot may stop, hover, allow the tail rotor to swing the fuselage through a half circle, then start going again in the opposite direction.

He can also make the turn without stopping. He pushes the stick a little to the side. This tips the rotor to the side. The copter leans inward, banking for the turn just as an airplane would.

AUTOROTATION

Finally, what about the story that a pilot can land safely even if his engine conks out and he has no power? It's so. If he handles the copter properly, he can make an autorotation landing. Autorotation means that the blades turn without help from the engine. But they will only do this if the copter is already moving.

Suppose the engine stops when the copter is about 500 feet up in the air. The pilot adjusts the blades so that they have very little pitch. At first they don't have much lift, and the copter begins to fall. But the falling motion soon acts on the blades as though they were at higher pitch, and the copter is supported just as before, but in a downward path, instead of level. With this downward motion there is enough pressure against the blades to keep them turning fairly fast—the way a pinwheel turns when you draw it through the air. The copter comes down in a long slow glide; when it is close to earth, the pilot suddenly increases the pitch of the blades.

Up to this point the blades have had speed but not enough lift to prevent the descent. The glide downward has given them whirling energy. Now the pilot trades speed for lift. By increasing pitch, he changes whirling energy into lifting energy. The copter stops gliding, and for a few moments it hovers. Then it drops straight down to the ground. This is called the flare-out. (Figure 18) If the pilot has judged everything correctly, he made the flare-out when the copter was just a few feet above the earth. And so the short drop did neither him nor the machine any harm.

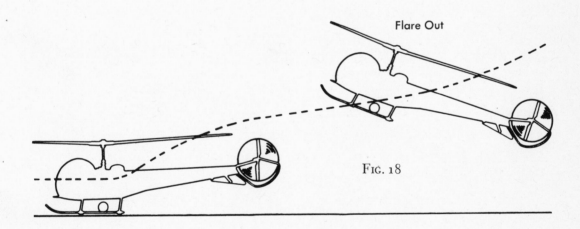

Flare Out

Fig. 18

THE SAME—ONLY DIFFERENT

So far, we've talked only about flying a copter that has a single two-bladed rotor. What about the others? From where the pilot sits, the principles of flying them all are pretty much the same. They all have a cyclic pitch lever, a combination throttle and collection pitch lever, and some kind of rudder control. In the next chapter you'll find out more about the differences between the various types.

12

SOLVING SOME PROBLEMS

MANY OF THE EARLY HELI-
copters had a somewhat nightmarish look about them. They make you wonder
if their inventors just cut loose with any wild fancy that came into their heads,
piling gadget on top of gimcrack.

Actually, nothing could be farther from the truth. Helicopter enthusiasts
have always been serious students of aeronautics. Every one of those queer
devices on their machines was intended to solve a problem.

It may have occurred to you already that a machine which can perform in
so many marvelous and unusual ways must be complicated. It is. The big
difference between the old-time machines and the new ones is this: On the
old ones the complicated machinery was showing. But today, modern engineers
have streamlined their problems. They have reduced large gadgets to small
automatic devices. It would take a long book to tell the whole fascinating story
of their work, but here are some special things you should know.

Take the problem of tipping the rotor in order to make the copter fly forward, backward or sideward. The early inventors used small propellers which
tipped the fuselage itself and the rotor along with it. This had the effect of
"aiming" the whole machine, the way you aim a helicopter toy.

We've already found out what modern engineers have done to solve the
same problem. They make the rotor blades alternately climb and dive in
cyclic pitch. This means that the blades can't be rigidly fixed the way the
spokes of a wheel are fixed tight to the hub that turns around the axle. There
must be a hinge which allows the blades to change their positions. Engineers
call one a flapping hinge, which permits the blade to rise and fall, or flap, as it

rotates. Another hinge, at right angles to the flapping hinge, is sometimes provided to let the blades move back and forth a little. To make sure this movement is small, the blades are equipped with a damper. It works like the gadget that keeps a door from slamming.

The picture shows you one type of hinge and damper. (Figure 1)

FIG. 1

Next, the pilot must have a control that regulates the climb and dive of the blades. It must change the pitch of each blade twice during each full circle of rotation. That's quite an order. Sikorsky solved the problem by linking the blades to flat plates which can be tilted up or down. The tilting of the plates changes the pitch of the blades. (Figure 2)

All of these remarkable inventions have been engineered into a very small inconspicuous space. They don't show up as the old-fashioned outside tilting propellers did, but they are much more complex.

FIG. 2

FIG. 3

Other manufacturers use different devices for changing blade pitch. A Bell copter, for example, has no individual hinges on the blades. Instead, the blades use a common hinge at the center of the hub. (Figure 3) The controls on a Kaman are not connected directly with the blades. Each blade is equipped with a sort of small wing called a servo-flap, which is linked to the control levers. The pilot changes the pitch of the flaps, and the flaps in turn make the blades rise up or dip down (Figure 4). A Hiller pilot uses stubby little control paddles to do the same jobs that the servo-flaps do (Figure 5).

FIG. 4

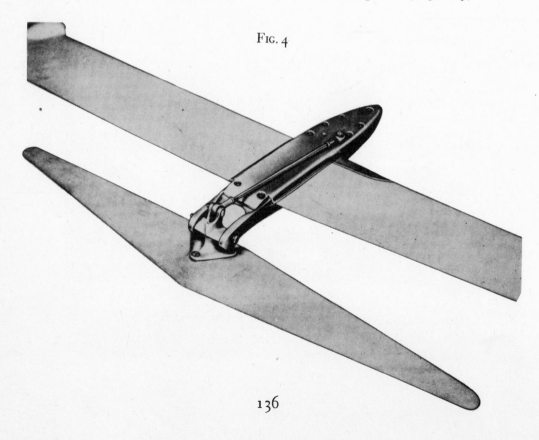

FIG. 5

HINGES AT WORK

The flapping hinge takes care of something else, too. It keeps the blades from snapping if the copter runs into rough air. Remember that the rotor lifts the weight of the fuselage and its passengers into the air. That puts a lot of strain on the blades. If they were held rigidly in place, the shock of bumpy air could break them. But the flapping hinge provides some "give."

Some helicopters have rotor blades that extend straight out horizontally when they are at rest. They may look rigid, but they aren't. When the copter takes off, the weight of the fuselage pulls downward at the middle of the rotor. The hinge allows the blades to take on the shape of a wide V as they whirl around. This is called *coning*. (Figure 6)

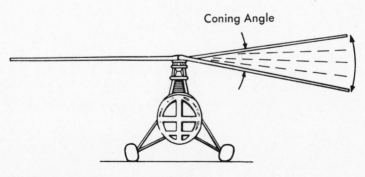

FIG. 6

You've probably noticed that other copters at rest on the ground have the look of an old floppy-eared dog. The blades droop. But in the air they perk up. These blades have two kinds of flexibility. They have flapping hinges, and they are also made of wood or metal that bends a little. At rest, they droop downward. In flight, the tips are pulled out straight. What pulls them? Centrifugal force. You can feel the pull of centrifugal force if you whirl a bucket tied to a rope. As the bucket moves faster, the rope straightens out.

On a helicopter, the outward pull of centrifugal force works against the downward pull of the fuselage. To see how, take a piece of string and hold one end in each hand. Then ask someone else to pull down at the middle of the string. Your hands, pulling outward on the ends, work against the downward pull at the middle. For the helicopter, the engineers have played one force against another to take some of the strain off the flapping hinge. This is true for the stiff blades as well as for the slightly flexible ones.

MORE THAN ONE ROTOR

The problem of torque reaction is something else that inventors have worked on in various ways. We've seen how a tail rotor does the trick. Here are some other designs:

Suppose you give the copter two big main rotors. Then you whirl them in opposite directions. The torque reaction of one cancels out the torque reaction of the other, and the problem is solved. This means you can throw away the tail rotor. But how can you steer the copter? You simply tilt the front rotor to one side in the direction you wish to turn, and tilt the rear rotor to the opposite side.

The two main rotors may be placed one above the other, with the axle of one inside the axle of the other. The photograph shows how this works. It's called a co-axial rotor system. (Figure 7)

Or the rotors may be bi-axial, which means the same engine turns both rotors, but on separate axles. In Figure 8 the rotors are mounted fore and aft, tandem-style, far enough apart so that their tips don't bump into each other.

In Figure 9 the rotors overlap. But they are made to turn without hitting each other, the way the blades of an eggbeater turn. They are called intermeshing rotors.

Figure 10 is another example of tandem rotors. One is mounted at the front of the fuselage, the other at the back. The same engine turns both.

FIG. 7

FIG. 8

FIG. 9

FIG. 10

Figure 11 has two rotors and two engines which turn the blades in opposite directions.

FIG. 11

All of these rotor systems *solve* the torque problem. But it's possible to build a machine that lacks it altogether. You simply give it two small jet engines mounted at the tips of the two blades. (Figure 12)

FIG. 12

A jet engine burns fuel very fast and puffs out a powerful jet of exhaust gas. That is the action. The reaction gives push to the blade—the way a shotgun kicks your shoulder. The pushing carries the blade forward at a high speed. But there is no torque reaction on the fuselage because the action doesn't come from an engine *inside* the fuselage.

POWER FOR WINGS

Jet engines are comparative newcomers to the helicopter world. In the beginning, helicopter inventors often took regular airplane engines, stood them up on end and put them to work. With an extra connection, the engine turned both the main rotor and the tail rotor. Or it turned two main rotors.

Thanks to all the research that aviation engineers have done with light metals, a modern airplane engine is a featherweight compared to the ones that had to be used even twenty years ago. Still, any copter engineer would love to get his hands on an even lighter one. The more his engine weighs, the less pay load his machine can carry.

Now the two little cigar-shaped jet engines weigh much less than one airplane engine that delivers the same amount of power. Jet units are much, much cheaper to make. It doesn't even pay to overhaul them—just throw them away and put on new ones. What's more, they can burn cheap fuel, such as kerosene, instead of expensive aviation gasoline. These things are all to the good.

Nevertheless, jet engineers have some unsolved problems. Jets gobble up fuel at low altitudes. This means a jet copter can carry more than a copter with a heavier engine, but it can't take the load as far in one hop, because it has to stop and refuel.

Other engineers are experimenting with turbo-jet power. This kind of jet is not attached directly to the blades. Instead, it uses its discharge of gas to whirl a turbine. Then the turbine whirls the rotor. A turbo-jet burns cheaper fuel than a gasoline engine. Possibly it will some day solve several problems at once. At any rate, the experimenters are hoping to come up with a light, cheap turbo-jet that gives a lot of power without being a pig for fuel.

HELPERS

Most people agree that helicopters are the safest aircraft even though they are the youngest. Does this mean they are easy to fly? Take a look at a copter pilot's arm muscles and you'll have the answer. The job of using the controls isn't heavy work, but the pilot can seldom relax for more than a few moments. That keeps his muscles in a class with a baseball player's. If he flies a single-rotor machine with a tail rotor, his feet have to be on the job all the time, too.

On the other hand, helicopter pilots generally prefer copters to fixed-wing craft. The whirlybirds give them a much greater sense of security, even though they can't fly "hands off."

So far only a few helicopters have any of the auto-pilot equipment that works so well on airplanes. The auto-pilot is made up of sensitive electrical devices linked with the plane's control system. The pilot sets everything for flight at a certain altitude, speed and direction. After that, the auto-pilot will adjust the controls if necessary—in case the plane hits some rough air, for example.

An auto-pilot is particularly useful when the helicopter has to hover in rough air. In the best of weather, hovering isn't as easy as it sounds. The pilot has to keep adjusting all his controls to hold the machine steady. An auto-pilot takes over some of these delicate adjustments and makes his work easier.

But even the lightest of automatic equipment adds some weight. As a rule, people who use helicopters want to carry as few extras as possible. They'd rather carry as big a pay load as they can.

For the same reason, most commercial helicopters don't carry special radio and night-flying equipment. They're still daytime machines for the most part. But even at night or in a fog the pilot can feel reasonably safe. He can fly low enough and slowly enough to keep his bearings. And he can always stop for a look around if he has to.

13

HOW YOU GET TO BE A PILOT

BACK IN THE MID-1940'S WHEN the helicopters first came along, many pilots of fixed-wing airplanes thought the whirlybird was a novelty, with no real value as a means of transportation. It was much too slow. Those same pilots also thought that all they had to do to learn how to fly a helicopter was to ride in one with an instructor for thirty or forty minutes, try out the controls, and then take off by themselves as qualified helicopter pilots.

A trip in a whirlybird quickly teaches a fixed-wing pilot that flying a helicopter is not that easy. It isn't hard, either, but it is different, very different from flying an airplane. For example, a pilot knows he has to fly an airplane at speeds of fifty, sixty—even ninety miles an hour—to keep it in the air. So you can see why many fixed-wing plane pilots have felt their hair stand up on end when they watched a whirlybird's airspeed indicator drop down to forty, thirty, twenty, ten, and then zero—and the helicopter still remained in the air and completely under control. The feeling that you must have forward speed to keep flying is one of the things a fixed-wing pilot has to unlearn when he becomes a helicopter pilot.

Strangely enough, however, the first step in learning to fly a helicopter is usually learning to fly a conventional airplane. Almost all helicopter pilots were private or commercial airplane pilots before they learned how to handle the copter. Their experience with fixed-wing aircraft taught them the "feel" of an airplane, and the developing of this sense of "feel" is important to all good and safe flying. It tells a pilot when he is flying too slowly to be safe. The same "feel" tells him also when his airplane is skidding in a turn. In a way, this sense of "feel" is similar to the sense you develop when you learn to ride a bicycle. When riding a bicycle is new to you, you feel unsteady and wobbly on it. You can't seem to steer it straight or make a turn without losing your balance. But after you have ridden for a while, you can do almost anything. You can steer around things; you can make sharp turns, and you can even ride it "Look—no hands!" That's because you have unconsciously learned the "feel" of riding a bicycle and are the complete master of it.

You develop this same sense of "feel" in flying an airplane. You learn to sense things and react to them in the right way almost without thinking. Old-time pilots call this "flying by the seat of the pants." No matter how many instruments are built into an airplane to tell a pilot how his airplane is flying, his own "feel" is very important. That is one of the reasons why knowing how to fly a conventional airplane is a good first step in learning how to fly a helicopter. It develops air-sense.

After you have learned to fly a fixed-wing airplane, studied weather and learned what the clouds in the sky mean, and also learned the Civil Air Regulations or the rules for flying the highways of the sky—then it's time to learn to fly the whirlybird. With your pilot's license—called a "ticket"—in your hand, you go to a helicopter school.

The first few lessons will be spent just going over the controls in the cockpit of the helicopter. Your instructor will explain the cyclic stick and show you how it controls the helicopter's movements forward, backward or sideways. He will explain the collective pitch lever and show you how it changes the pitch of the whirlybird's main rotor to make the copter climb or descend. He will show you how the rudder makes the copter turn to the right or left.

Your instructor will take you up in the helicopter and show you all the maneuvers that only a whirlybird can do. Now you're ready to try it yourself, with the instructor sitting right there to help.

FIRST FLIGHT

In the beginning, you'll take the helicopter only a few feet off the ground. You will learn how to use all the controls together and to perform the maneuvers smoothly and easily. At first a student helicopter pilot over-controls his machine. He uses too much rudder or too much pitch in the main rotor. A first attempt at straight and level flight, even if it is only six or ten feet off the ground, will probably look more like an old-fashioned shoot-the-chutes on a roller coaster than the straight and level flight of a veteran copter pilot on a pipe-line patrol job. The first few times you handle the controls, your motions will be just as unsteady and wobbly as they were when you learned to ride the bicycle. You may make your instructor think he is riding a canoe on a choppy lake, but very soon your wobbles will change into the same ease and smoothness you finally achieved in riding that bike.

144

PARK HERE

After you have learned how to use the controls together and your forward flight is smooth and easy, the next step is hovering flight. Here again, just as in every other maneuver, your first tries will be rough. But as you practice holding the helicopter in hovering flight—first with the rudder alone, then with cyclic stick and rudder, then with pitch and throttle alone, and finally, with all the controls together—you'll find yourself able to "sit still" over some spot as though you had decided to park there and watch a ball game.

Then will come stops and starts, vertical landing, vertical take-offs and sideways and rearward flight.

In teaching you sideways and rearward flight, your instructor will point out the edge of a runway or perhaps a road running through open country, and he will ask you to follow the line of the runway or the road for several hundred feet sideways and then rearward. When you first try it, the instructor will probably comment that the scallops you're making would be nice on a little girl's dress, but that they have no place in the maneuvers of a whirlybird. Practice and more practice soon will straighten out your sideways and rearward lines, and the scallops will be finally and completely erased.

Next will come lessons in how to make steep turns, how to hover over a spot and not drift away from it when a wind is blowing at you from the side or from the rear. You will learn how to fly perfectly square patterns and how to land and take off when the wind is coming from the side or from the back instead of from directly ahead of you. This is known as landing and taking off crosswind and downwind.

SOLO

When you have learned these lessons well, your instructor will step out of the helicopter and tell you to go ahead and fly the whirlybird all by yourself. To make up for the loss of his weight in the machine, he'll put in a sandbag or some weight that is about the same as his. He does this so that the copter will handle itself the same way it did when he was with you.

Remembering all the things your instructor taught you, you will take off vertically, then hover at an altitude of about six feet to check all the conditions of the engine and controls. Then you will accelerate to forty-five or fifty miles per hour and climb to whatever altitude the instructor has requested. After that, you will follow the airport traffic pattern, descend at about forty miles per hour, level off at an altitude of six feet for several seconds, and then land. When you are firmly on the ground, have cut the engine, and the rotor has stopped turning, everyone at the field will probably be there to shake your hand and compliment you on a very excellent flight.

At this point you are one-half a helicopter pilot, and the days that follow will be filled with more lessons in more maneuvers: steep turns; how to make slow but steep approaches to a landing area or heliport; and how to taxi a helicopter. You will learn how to land your helicopter safely if its engine should suddenly stop, and how to take off and land on a rough field in case you decide you want to crop-dust or ride herd on the cattle at a ranch.

With these lessons well learned, now is the time to demonstrate to your local Civil Aeronautics Authority Aviation Safety Agent your ability to fly a helicopter. This done, he will add a helicopter rating to your private or commercial pilot's license. A rating is just a stamp that says you can fly one. And now you are a whole helicopter pilot.

From now on it's up to you to practice flying the copter until you become better and better at it. Soon you will be as good as the four Bell flyers who actually square-danced their whirlybirds to music and the calls at an air show. The four helicopters "bowed to their partners," "bowed to their corners," did "first and third ladies forward and back," then "second and fourth gents forward and back," and finally performed a "promenade all." And while they "danced," the whirlybirds were fifty feet above the ground.

"Bow to your partner . . . bow to your corner," and four Bells square dance to music.

Some helicopter pilots want to know how to repair their copters if anything goes wrong. Other people just want to learn how to do repair work without learning how to fly. Most helicopter mechanics were aircraft and engine mechanics before they became copter mechanics, just as the pilots were airplane pilots before they became helicopter pilots.

These aircraft and engine mechanics, called A and E's by the pilots, go to schools that are located in the factories of the companies that build the helicopters. If an A and E wants to be a mechanic for Bell helicopters, he goes to a school at the Bell factory in Texas. If he wants to work on Sikorsky helicopters, he goes to the Sikorsky factory for instruction. At these schools, students learn how to keep the whirlybirds flying by actually working on them at the factory. Their teachers are the men who helped build the copters themselves.

Whirlybird pilots and whirlybird mechanics think first and always of their machines. No father takes better care of his son, no mother hen takes better care of her chicks, than a pilot and mechanic of their willing whirlybird.

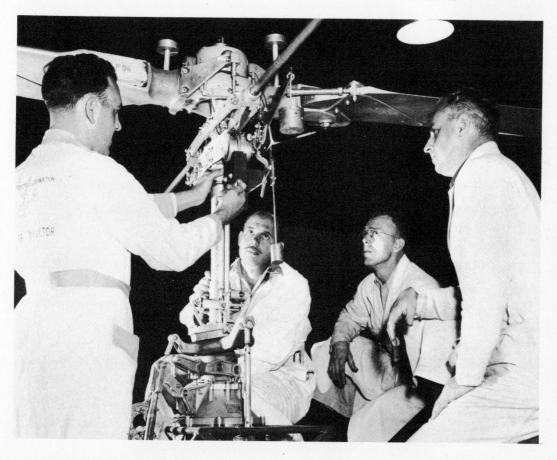

Copter mechanics learn their trade in factories where the whirlybirds are built.

147

14

LOOKING AHEAD

BY NOW YOU PROBABLY WANT to know: "What are the chances that I can have a whirlybird of my own?"

That depends. If you were rich enough, you could order one and have it delivered in a few months. But will there ever be common, garden-variety helicopters on the market for the price of a good car? Some day there are sure to be, but how soon, nobody can really say.

We know that so-called personal helicopters have been invented. There is one kind that is supposed to waltz you along over the treetops while you sit on a sort of bicycle frame, with the rotor buzzing just over your head. Military people have been particularly interested in small, light, inexpensive machines, and lots of experimenting has been done with them. The results of these experiments have not been shown to the public. One type is supposed to zoom around like an oversized horsefly, and apparently it is so easy to control that the pilot can fly it with almost no effort at all.

Still, it will be a while before you can count on keeping one of these in your garage. Some people in the helicopter business cautiously predict that you can forget this wonderful thought for many, many years. Others, like the Glenview people of Delanco, New Jersey, who are concentrating their efforts on an easy-to-fly, one-stick-control helicopter for civilians, say there should be a medium-priced eggbeater on the market in five years, provided we don't get into a war. One big hotel owner in Texas is so sure of this that he has put a heliport on the roof of his new building!

NEW USES

Meantime, you will see more and more helicopters doing wonderful every-day chores—old chores and new ones. At a conference of fire chiefs not long

Twin-engine Sikorsky S-56 is as big as a DC-3; can carry 26 at speed of 150 mph.

ago, proposals were made for fire-copters. Whirlybirds would carry fire fighters up where they wouldn't have to worry about traffic in crowded city streets. The copters could hover and extinguish blazes in the upper stories of tall buildings.

More mail may be delivered quickly by helicopter in the future, not just near a few big cities, but in many parts of the country that in the past have always had slow service.

Other cities will probably get copters for their police departments. In New York City, a fleet of whirlybirds has been doing all kinds of police work. They have rescued boys who lost their oars while rowing on the river. They have patrolled crowded beaches, cruised around keeping an eye out for danger among the hundreds of boats and ships in the busy harbor. A cop in a copter even gave a traffic ticket to the pilot of a light plane who broke some rules and flew dangerously over the city. And more and more helicopters in the future will certainly be cruising around to straighten out traffic snarls.

SKY BUSES

Bigger and better sky buses are certainly on the way. One type will probably have a section called a pod which will be able to be attached or detached to the main body of the copter like a truck trailer, except that it will be underneath and not at the back. The pod will carry either extra passengers or cargo. One expert has estimated that by 1965 huge eggbeaters will be ferrying six million passengers to and from New York City every year! No one can begin to add up the other millions who may be lifted in and out of other cities.

Some of these future copter buses may possibly carry as many as a hundred

British-made Bristol Type 171 carries pilot and four passengers at 123 mph.

people, but they will probably be unusual. A more likely number of seats is forty or fifty. The manufacturers already have drawings that show what could be built. One type has twin engines and two rotors—one in front and one in back. Another has a single big rotor that is turned by jet engines. Dr. Hugh Dryden of the National Advisory Committee for Aeronautics predicts that new forms of jet propulsion may be developed, so that the helicopter's rotors, like the propeller, will disappear within the next fifty years!

One thing is clear—you'll ride in comfort, although you may not travel at high speeds. The experts feel that a copter which jogs along at two hundred miles an hour is going fast enough, for the immediate future, at least.

Engines of England's Westland 85 are six gas turbines mounted in pairs on rotor tips.

150

Aerial inter-city bus of the future may be this jet-rotor helicopter from England.

CONVERTIPLANES

One way to put on more speed is to change a helicopter into a fixed-wing craft after it has got off to an almost vertical start in the air. Machines of this sort are called convertiplanes, heliplanes, planicopters, or just plain convertible aircraft.

Remember the old autogyro, which had both wings and a rotor? It wasn't really a convertiplane, because its rotor had no power. A true convertible aircraft is one which combines both rotary and fixed wings. One was actually built and flown over twenty years ago. By the time you read this, new ones may even be flying.

Bristol Type 173 is a 16-passenger copter built for airline use in Great Britain.

Planned for the future, this jet Gyrodyne is under development today in England.

One convertiplane has rotor blades that whirl round for take-off and descent. But when the craft is in the air, the blades can be stopped and held stiff, so that they act like regular airplane wings, while a propeller in the nose pulls the craft forward.

Another type has its rotors mounted near the tips of fixed wings. For take-off and landing, and for slow or hovering flight, the rotors whirl like ordinary helicopter rotors. But for fast speed forward, the rotors tilt forward until they take on the position of regular propellers. Then they pull the craft ahead.

Designed for easy flying, this two-place "Fly-ride" may one day be your second car.

Tests aboard the HMS Eagle *proved the Bristol Type 173 has built-in sea legs.*

Four gas turbines power the "Quadrotor," a convertiplane for future airline use.

The third type has wings, plus a rotor that folds down into the fuselage when it is not needed. Regular propellers or jets then take over the job of moving the craft through the air.

Still another convertiplane idea looks as if it came out of science-fiction, but the idea is not impossible. The craft is supposed to take off straight up in the air like a rocket, which it resembles. Then it levels off, the rotors act like wings, and propellers take over.

The four rotors intermesh on Convertawings' smaller version of this "Quadrotor."

Rotor gives the XV-1 its vertical lift; the pusher propeller, its forward flight.

This eight-passenger gas-propelled whirlybird is under construction in England.

First came Cierva's autogyro, and now we have his large triple-rotor "Air Horse."

Bristol's transport helicopter can carry its passengers a distance of 435 miles.

The British tested this Cierva-Weir experimental jet torque-reaction model in 1946.

Aviation people all over the United States have begun to think and plan for the future. They are discussing locations for heliports and how to build them. You probably know that there is a well-established body of rules and regulations for airports and for the fixed-wing aircraft that use them. There still isn't any such thing for helicopters, although there will be soon. Government officials are working on regulations now.

Whirlybird enthusiasts hope they can keep the rules as simple as possible. Suppose that the various states all got excited and worked out different ones! A pilot would find it hard to memorize forty-eight complete sets of regulations.

Actually the problem of rules isn't as difficult as it sounds. Helicopters can surely operate out of regular airports without getting in the way of fixed-wing traffic. For one thing, they can approach the field from a much lower altitude, and they can stop and wait if they have to. An enormous amount of thought has already gone into figuring out ways to make flight safe for droves of copters —when they come.

One person who believes they are coming before long is Igor Sikorsky. He is so confident about the future, because he himself built a helicopter when most people thought it was either impractical or foolish. As a joke on them, he has put up in his factory a sign that says:

"According to recognized aerotechnical tests, the bumblebee cannot fly because of the shape and weight of his body in relation to the total wing area. But the bumblebee doesn't know this, so he goes ahead and flies anyway."

So—if anybody says you probably won't ever get that eggbeater of your own, remember the bumblebee.

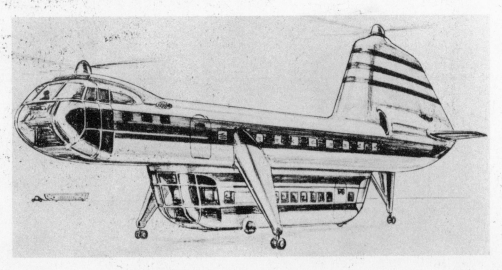

Passengers will ride in the detachable pod of this airline version of the YH-16.

MORE ABOUT HELICOPTERS

IF YOU want to know more about helicopters, here are some books that you will enjoy reading:

The How of the Helicopter, by Alfred H. Stevens, published by the Cornell Maritime Press. An easily understood story of why and how a copter flies, together with explanations of mechanical principles.

Helicopter Guide, by C. L. Morris, published by Helicopter Utilities, Inc., Box 109, White Plains, New York. Further details about the workings of a copter, plus interesting material on how to fly one.

Pioneering the Helicopter, by C. L. Morris, published by McGraw-Hill Book Company. The story of Igor Sikorsky and the men who worked with him to develop Sikorsky machines. Filled with amusing anecdotes.

The Story of the Helicopter, by Devon Francis, published by Coward-McCann, Inc. Much history, particularly of American experiments up to 1946.

Flying Windmills, by Frank Ross, Jr., published by Lothrop, Lee & Shepard Co. More history and stories of inventors up to the present.

. . . . .

A 16 mm. movie called "The History of the Helicopter" can be obtained by schools and libraries from the Shell Oil Company.

Aviation films can also be obtained from the University of Illinois Visual Aids Service, Champaign, Illinois.

HELICOPTER SCHOOLS

IF YOU want to learn to fly a helicopter, here is a list of schools that have been approved by the Civil Aeronautics Administration:

East Coast Aviation Corporation
Bedford Airport
Lexington, Massachusetts

Lyons Flying School
Zahn's Airfield
Lindenhurst, New York

Nashua Aviation & Supply
Boire Field
Nashua, New Hampshire

New England Helicopter Service, Inc.
State Airport
Hillsgrove, Rhode Island

Petroleum Bell Helicopter Services, Inc.
Lafayette, Louisiana

J. D. Reed Company, Inc.
Municipal Airport, Hangar 8
Houston, Texas

Rick Helicopters, Inc.
13440 South Central Avenue
Los Angeles, California

Sky Haven Flying School, Inc.
R.F.D. 58
Woods Cross, Utah

Westair Flying School, Inc.
Westchester County Airport
White Plains, New York

E. W. Wiggins Airways, Inc.
Norwood, Massachusetts

HELICOPTER COUNCIL

AIRCRAFT INDUSTRIES ASSOCIATION OF AMERICA, INC.
610 SHOREHAM BUILDING, WASHINGTON 5, D. C.

Chairman: Charles H. Kaman
Vice Chairman: Stanley Hiller, Jr.

MEMBER COMPANIES

Bell Aircraft Corporation
Helicopter Division
P. O. Box 482
Fort Worth 1, Texas
Harvey Gaylord, Vice President

Cessna Aircraft Company
Helicopter Division
Wichita, Kansas
J. E. Leonard, Manager

Doman Helicopters, Inc.
P. O. Box 603
Municipal Airport
Danbury, Connecticut
Glidden S. Doman, President

Hiller Helicopters
1350 Willow Road
Palo Alto, California
Stanley Hiller, Jr., President

Kaman Aircraft Corporation
Bradley Field
Windsor Locks, Connecticut
Charles H. Kaman, President

McDonnell Aircraft Corporation
Lambert-St. Louis Airport
P. O. Box 516
St. Louis 3, Missouri
J. S. McDonnell, President

Piasecki Helicopter Corporation
Morton, Pennsylvania
F. N. Piasecki
Chairman of the Board

Sikorsky Aircraft Division
United Aircraft Corporation
Bridgeport 1, Connecticut
B. L. Whelan, General Manager

Hughes Tool Company
Aeronautical Division
Culver City, California
R. E. Hopper, Director

ABOUT THE AUTHOR

D. N. AHNSTROM, born in Muskegon, Michigan, has been an aviation writer and editor for the past fifteen years and is presently Managing Editor of *Skyways*, a technical trade publication devoted to flight operations. The author learned to fly at Floyd Bennett Field, New York, in 1937 while a member of the staff of the New York *Daily News*; became a member of the Aircraft Owners and Pilots Association in 1937, and joined the staff of *Skyways* in 1942. The author became an affiliate of the Institute of Aeronautical Sciences and a member of the Aviation Writers Association in 1944.

THIS BOOK was composed in Electra and Futura types by Westcott & Thomson, Inc., Philadelphia. Printed on Perkins and Squire Special offset paper stock by Copifyer Lithograph Corporation, Cleveland, Ohio and bound by The Press of The World Publishing Company, Cleveland, Ohio.

3 4 5 6 7 8 9 10 65 64 63 62 61 60 59 58